CollegeBoard

SpringBoard™

Mathematics with Meaning™

Middle School Mathematics I
Student Version

The College Board: Connecting Students to College Success

The College Board is a not-for-profit membership association whose mission is to connect students to college success and opportunity. Founded in 1900, the association is composed of more than 4,700 schools, colleges, universities, and other educational organizations. Each year, the College Board serves over three and a half million students and their parents, 23,000 high schools, and 3,500 colleges through major programs and services in college admissions, guidance, assessment, financial aid, enrollment, and teaching and learning. Among its best-known programs are the SAT®, the PSAT/NMSQT®, and the Advanced Placement Program® (AP®). The College Board is committed to the principles of excellence and equity, and that commitment is embodied in all of its programs, services, activities, and concerns.

Please be advised that the SpringBoard materials are updated periodically. We encourage you to contact the SpringBoard program to ensure you have the latest version.

For further information, visit www.collegeboard.com.

ISBN-13: 978-0-87447-811-2
ISBN-10: 0-87447-811-1

Mathematics with Meaning – Middle School Mathematics I

ACKNOWLEDGMENTS

The College Board gratefully acknowledges the expertise, time, and commitment of the following committee members:

James R. Choike
Professor of Mathematics
Oklahoma State University
Stillwater, OK

Marcia Chumas
Mathematics Teacher
East Mecklenburg High School
Charlotte, NC

Betty Davis
Mathematics Teacher
Boston Latin School
Boston, MA

Wendy DenBesten
Mathematics Teacher
Hoover High School
Fresno, CA

Theresa Fox
Mathematics Teacher
Torrington Middle School
Torrington, WY

Megan Gerstenzang
Mathematics Teacher
Gibbons Middle School
Westborough, MA

Jill Gough
Mathematics Teacher
The Westminster Schools
Atlanta, GA

Sam Gough
Mathematics Teacher
The Westminster Schools
Atlanta, GA

Andrew Kearns
Mathematics Teacher
Dr. Michael M. Krop Sr. High
School
Miami, FL

Guy Mauldin
Mathematics Teacher
Science Hill High School
Johnson City, TN

Dean Packard
Mathematics Teacher
Tucson High Magnet School
Tucson, AZ

Chris Sollars
Mathematics Teacher
Alamo Heights High School
San Antonio, TX

Jill Stevens
Mathematics Teacher
Trinity High School
Euless, TX

Andrea Sukow
Mathematics Coordinator
Metro Nashville Public Schools
Nashville, TN

Sue Swanda
Mathematics Teacher
Vance High School
Charlotte, NC

Judy Windle
Mathematics Consultant
East Mecklenburg High School
Charlotte, NC

The College Board gratefully acknowledges the expertise, time, and commitment of the editor for mathematics materials:

Nina Hnatov
Editor
Glen Head, NY

The College Board recognizes the contributions of the following individuals as integral to the development and review of the mathematics materials:

Benita Albert
Mathematics Teacher
Oak Ridge High School
Oak Ridge, TN

Terri Breeden
Executive Director
Metropolitan Nashville Public
Schools
Nashville, TN

Sandy Campo
Mathematics Consultant
Providence, RI

John Dossey
Professor of Mathematics
Illinois State University
Normal, IL

Kay Fenton
Mathematics Dept Chair
Episcopal High School
Baton Rouge, LA

Landy Godbold
Mathematics Teacher
The Westminster School
Atlanta, GA

Christopher Kribs-Zaleta
Associate Professor of
Mathematics
University of Texas at
Arlington
Arlington, TX

Dallice Lazarus
Mathematics Teacher
Rye Country Day School
Rye, NY

Guy Mauldin
Mathematics Teacher
Science Hill High School
Johnson City, TN

Claire Pollard
Mathematics Consultant
Providence, RI

Beverly Smith
Mathematics Specialist
Alaska Dept of Education and
Early Development
Juneau, AK

J. T. Sutcliffe
Mathematics Teacher
The St. Mark's School of
Texas
Dallas, TX

Tony Terceira
Mathematics Consultant
Providence, RI

Beverly Whittington
Mathematics Consultant
Educational Testing Service
Moorestown, NJ

This material is based on work supported by the National Science Foundation under Grant No. 0243479.

Mathematics with Meaning – Middle School Mathematics I

TABLE OF CONTENTS

Middle School Mathematics I

Introduction

Overview

Succeeding in college is important.

But just as important is *preparing* for success.

That is what the College Board's new SpringBoard™ program is all about — building the critical thinking skills in reading, writing and mathematics that lead to success in Advanced Placement courses and college.

SpringBoard maps out what successful students should know and be able to do at each grade level to succeed in college-level work, including Advanced Placement courses. We call these rigorous standards the College Board Standards for College Success™.

When you use SpringBoard's unique tools, you will:

- Participate in interactive, student-centered units of instruction
- Learn the reading, writing, problem solving, and collaborative strategies that help you best as a learner
- Take a variety of diagnostic assessments that provide information to you, your teacher, and your parents about your progress

Discover how SpringBoard can help you achieve high academic standards, reach your goals, and prepare for success.

Standards for College Success

The College Board Standards for College Success™ describe a developmental progression of quantitative skills and mathematics concepts that you should master to be ready for success in college-level work, either during high school in Advanced Placement courses or during your freshman year in college. Within each Standard are thematic Strands, which develop a set of related process or content skills. The Strands have been conceived at a level of granularity that will support meaningful diagnostic assessments and effective instruction.

Standards for College Success

Standard: Number and Operations

Students study number systems, operations in these systems, and computation within these systems. They forge links by application of number and operations proficiencies to other areas of mathematics and the curriculum.

Strand: Number

Strand: Operations

Strand: Computation and Estimation

Strand: Problem Solving

Strand: Representations

Strand: Reasoning and Proof

Strand: Communication

Standard: Algebra

Students move from thinking about concrete quantities and arithmetic operations to thinking about and visualizing "quantity" in more general ways. Part of this transition is the development of the students' capabilities to visualize, abstract, and generalize representations.

Strand: Patterns and Relations

Strand: Variables, Expressions, Equations, and Inequalities

Strand: Functions with Growth and Change

Strand: Problem Solving

Strand: Representations

Strand: Reasoning and Proof

Strand: Communication

Standard: Geometry

Geometry is the study of shapes: their properties, their location in space, and the relationships among shapes.

Strand: Properties, Attributes, and Models of Plane and Solid Figures

Strand: Problem Solving

Strand: Representations

Strand: Reasoning and Proof

Strand: Communication

Standard: Measurement

An important aspect of mathematics and quantitative reasoning involves measurement, including length, area, volume, capacity, weight/mass, and time.

> **Strand: Measurement Units and Systems**
> **Strand: Applications of Measurement**
> **Strand: Conversions with Measures**
> **Strand: Problem Solving**
> **Strand: Representations**
> **Strand: Reasoning and Proof**
> **Strand: Communication**

Standard: Data Analysis and Probability

Students collect, organize, summarize, and interpret data. To emphasize the spirit of statistical thinking, students begin their data analysis with a question to be answered, not with the data.

> **Strand: Data Collection**
> **Strand: Data Exploration**
> **Strand: Data Interpretation**
> **Strand: Probability Concepts and Applications**
> **Strand: Problem Solving**
> **Strand: Representations**
> **Strand: Reasoning and Proof**
> **Strand: Communication**

Learning Strategies

INTRODUCTION

The SpringBoard™ system has high standards and challenging material at its core; therefore, it is imperative that these Model Instructional Units equip students and teachers with the skills to meet these standards. The *Reading*, *Writing*, *Problem Solving*, and *Collaborative* learning strategies, embedded within the Units, represent the latest research and best teaching practices. But strategies alone, without content, have been shown to be less than effective. Instead, the Model Instructional Units included in the *Mathematics with Meaning* program infuse these learning strategies so that they are fully embedded into the lessons that teachers are facilitating in their classrooms. Additionally, the materials identify the strategies being used in each lesson by a series of icons, to assist teachers in becoming familiar with the purpose of each strategy and to recognize those that are most beneficial to their students.

A list of the strategies, including a definition for each, a purpose for using the particular strategic approach, and an icon that will help to identify that particular strategy, are located in Appendix I. A list of icons and their associated strategy names is found on the following page.

Learning Strategies

READING

❶ Chunking the Text

❷ Graphic Organizer

❸ KWL Chart (Know, Want, Learn Chart)

❹ Marking the Text

❺ PACA (Predicting and Confirming Activity)

❻ Questioning the Text

❼ Read and Think Aloud

❽ Role Play

❾ Summarizing/Paraphrasing/Retelling

❿ Visualization

PROBLEM SOLVING

1 Act Out the Problem

2 Draw a Sketch

3 Guess and Check

4 Identify a Subtask

5 Look for a Pattern

6 Make a Table or Organized List

7 Simplify the Problem

8 Work Backward

9 Write a Number Sentence

WRITING

1 Graphic Organizer

2 Journal

3 Quickwrite

4 RAFT (Role of Writer, Audience, Format, and Topic)

5 Self-Editing/Peer Editing

COLLABORATIVE

1 Debriefing

2 Group Presentation

3 Jigsaw

4 Think-Pair-Share

Middle School Mathematics I

Model Instructional Units

Middle School Mathematics I

Egg Cartons

Contents

Egg Cartons

STUDENT ACTIVITY

Part I

Your class has been called to help the *Chanticleer Egg Farm* with some marketing decisions. The management has decided to try to improve its business by redesigning their egg cartons and wants your help.

1. Measure the length and width of a standard egg carton.

   a. If the egg carton is "six eggs long," about how long is one egg's worth of carton?

   b. If the egg carton is "two eggs wide," about how wide is one egg's worth of carton? Is this measure the same as in Part (a)?

2. If the egg delivery truck has trays measuring 8 inches × 24 inches (20 cm × 61 cm), how many eggs will fit in the tray? How will the eggs be arranged? Explain below.

3. Sometimes a grocer will sell eggs by the half dozen instead of by the dozen. Some egg cartons are actually perforated to make splitting the carton easier.

   a. How many different ways can the grocer split a standard 12-egg carton in half, using one straight cut? Draw figures to show how each carton should be cut.

   b. How many different ways can the grocer split a standard 12-egg carton into thirds, using one straight cut? Draw figures to show how each carton should be cut.

4. Consider other possible designs for 12-egg cartons. The cartons must be rectangular, hold exactly 12 eggs, and have a hinge on one side for the lid. What other possible designs (configurations) are there? Draw the design arrangements, and indicate the location of the hinges.

5. The numbers 2 and 3 are called **factors** of 12 because 12 is divisible by each number. In other words, when 12 is divided by 2 or by 3, the results are whole numbers.

   a. List all of the factors of 12.

   b. List all of the factors of 6.

   c. Explain why each factor of 6 is also a factor of 12.

Part II

6. The *Chanticleer Egg Farm* is considering selling eggs in cartons containing other amounts.

    a. How many eggs can be packaged together if the egg cartons are to be square?

    b. Which of the square arrangements in Part (a) do you recommend, and why?

7. Bakers used to include an extra roll in every bag of 12 rolls sold, in case the rolls did not weigh enough (they sold rolls by weight). This gave rise to the term "a baker's dozen," meaning 13. The farm is considering selling eggs by the baker's dozen, so there will still be a dozen good eggs even if one egg breaks. How many hinged rectangular cartons will hold exactly 13 eggs? Explain below.

Egg Cartons

8. Fill in the table below to show the number of possible design arrangements for an egg carton for each number of eggs.

Number of Eggs	Possible Hinged Carton Arrangements	Number of Arrangements
1		
2		
3		
4		
5		
6		
7		
8		
9		
10		
11		
12		
13		
14		
15		
16		
17		
18		
19		
20		
21		
22		
23		
24		
25		

9. Refer to the table in Question 8 to answer the following questions.

    a. Which numbers of eggs only allow two carton arrangements?

    b. What do these numbers have in common?

    c. Why do they only allow two arrangements?

10. The numbers in your response to Question 9 are called **prime** numbers.

    a. List the prime numbers between 26 and 50.

    b. Explain your procedure for identifying the prime numbers in Part (a).

11. Which numbers in the table in Question 8 allow more than two arrangements?

12. Which numbers in the table in Question 8 allow the largest numbers of different arrangements?

13. What do numbers that allow more than two arrangements have in common?

Egg Cartons

STUDENT ACTIVITY (continued)

14. The numbers in your response to Question 13 are called **composite** numbers.

    a. Write a definition for composite numbers.

    b. How are composite numbers different from prime numbers?

15. What determines how many arrangements will be possible?

16. The farm wants to sell eggs in cartons that hold three dozen eggs.

    a. How many different carton arrangements are possible? Explain below.

    b. Which carton arrangements for 36 eggs do you recommend? Why?

Egg Cartons

The *Chanticleer Egg Farm* has asked you to make a recommendation for how many eggs to package in a single carton. In making your recommendation, consider two criteria: (1) whether a "nice" carton can be made for that number of eggs, and (2) whether the carton can be cut easily into halves or thirds, like a standard egg carton can.

17. Write a report to the *Chanticleer Egg Farm* explaining your recommendation, based on their criteria.

Egg Cartons

Title of Model Instructional Unit: Egg Cartons

Embedded Assessment Question # _____ Page # _____

How could you improve your response to this question?

What part of this Model Instructional Unit is an example of your best work? Explain why you feel this is your best work.

What mathematical skills, strategies, or knowledge that you had prior to starting this Model Instructional Unit helped you to complete this activity?

What new mathematical skills, strategies, or knowledge did you obtain while completing this Model Instructional Unit?

Middle School Mathematics I

I'll Take...You'll Take...

Contents

I'll Take...You'll Take...

Part I

Your teacher challenges the entire class to a game of *I'll Take...You'll Take....* Your teacher knows the rules of the game, but you do not. You will have to discover the rules as you play.

Teacher Score   *I'll Take...You'll Take...*   **Class Score**

1	2	3	4	5
6	7	8	9	10
11	12	13	14	15
16	17	18	19	20
21	22	23	24	25
26	27	28	29	30
31	32	33	34	35
36	37	38	39	40
41	42	43	44	45
46	47	48	49	50

I'll Take...You'll Take...

1. After playing several rounds of the game, answer the following questions.

   a. Explain what it means for one number to be a factor of another number.

   b. List all pairs of positive factors of each number below.

   13   49

   24   36

   75   40

   31   48

   50   47

2. Write a set of rules for playing and scoring the game *I'll Take...You'll Take....*

3. Which numbers in Question 1(b) have only one pair of factors?

4. Write a strategy that will help you win the game *I'll Take...You'll Take....*

Part II

Finding factors of numbers is a useful skill for the game *I'll Take...You'll Take...* and for many problems in mathematics. Answer the following questions.

5. a. Circle the numbers below that have 2 as a factor.

   14   18   27   45   96   89   16   68   25

   b. What do you notice about all the numbers you circled?

6. a. Circle the numbers below that have 5 as a factor.

   34   65   70   54   96   80   27   45   15

   b. What do you notice about all the numbers you circled?

7. a. Circle the numbers below that have 10 as a factor.

   14   10   27   40   90   89   32   60   38

   b. What do you notice about all the numbers you circled?

8. a. Circle the numbers below that have 3 as a factor.

65   27   51   74   57   92   116   321   105

b. Find the sum of the digits of each of the numbers that you circled and describe what you notice.

9. a. Circle the numbers below that have 9 as a factor.

14   18   27   99   96   89   115   891   1998

b. Find the sum of the digits of each of the numbers that you circled and describe what you notice.

10. a. Circle the numbers below that have 4 as a factor.

165   312   516   474   124   106   132   384   192

b. Write the numbers formed by the last two digits of each of the numbers that you circled and describe what you notice about these numbers.

11. a. We say that 40 is divisible by 10 because 40 divided by 10 has a remainder of 0. List some other numbers that are divisible by 10.

b. A **divisibility rule** is a shortcut for quickly recognizing when one number is divisible by another. Write a divisibility rule for 10.

12. Write a divisibility rule for each of the following numbers.

    2

    3

    4

    5

    9

13. Write a divisibility rule for the number 6.

14. a. The numbers you listed in Question 3 are called **prime numbers**. Define a prime number.

    b. What is the smallest prime number?

I'll Take...You'll Take...

Part III

15. In the third century BC, a famous mathematician named Eratosthenes developed a routine to list prime numbers. To use his method, the *Sieve of Eratosthenes*, the numbers two through 100 are listed in the table below. Circle the number two, which is the first prime number. Cross out every number on the table that is a multiple of two. Circle the next number not crossed out. It should be the number three, which is the next prime number. Cross out every number that is a multiple of three. The next number not crossed out is the next prime number. Circle this number and repeat the process until you sift out all of the primes through 100.

Sieve of Eratosthenes

	2	3	4	5	6
7	8	9	10	11	12
13	14	15	16	17	18
19	20	21	22	23	24
25	26	27	28	29	30
31	32	33	34	35	36
37	38	39	40	41	42
43	44	45	46	47	48
49	50	51	52	53	54
55	56	57	58	59	60
61	62	63	64	65	66
67	68	69	70	71	72
73	74	75	76	77	78
79	80	81	82	83	84
85	86	87	88	89	90
91	92	93	94	95	96
97	98	99	100		

16. List all of the prime numbers less than 100 from the table in Question 15.

17. Play the game *I'll Take...You'll Take...* again. What number did you choose first? Explain your choice.

18. The education department of a board game company has decided to market the game of *I'll Take...You'll Take...*. Since you are now an expert at the game, the company has asked you to do some work for them. Write a set of instructions and a set of strategies for the game. Given that the company is trying to sell *I'll Take...You'll Take...* as an educational game, be sure as you write your instructions and strategies that you include the math concepts that you have just worked on.

I'll Take...You'll Take...

Title of Model Instructional Unit: I'll Take...You'll Take...

Embedded Assessment Question # _____ Page # _____

How could you improve your response to this question?

What part of this Model Instructional Unit is an example of your best work? Explain why you feel this is your best work.

What mathematical skills, strategies, or knowledge that you had prior to starting this Model Instructional Unit helped you to complete this activity?

What new mathematical skills, strategies, or knowledge did you obtain while completing this Model Instructional Unit?

Middle School Mathematics I

A Fairly Ordered Operation

Contents

A Fairly Ordered Operation

Introduction

The Pace County Fair charges a general admission of $8.00 per person. The general admission price covers the cost of visiting exhibits and some entertainment. Tickets for rides and games must be purchased at an additional cost. Cash may be used to purchase food and drinks at the concession stands.

Part I

The cost of a ride ticket is $3.00.

1. Complete the table below to show the cost of attending the fair with the given number of ride tickets purchased.

Number of Ride Tickets Purchased	Cost of Attending the Fair (in dollars)
0	8
1	8 + 3 = 11
2	8 + 3 + 3 = 14
3	
4	
5	
6	

2. Do you notice a pattern in the Cost of Attending the Fair column? Explain below.

A Fairly Ordered Operation

STUDENT ACTIVITY (continued)

3. The cost of attending the fair and buying two ride tickets can be expressed as 8 + 3 + 3. Since only two numbers can be added at one time, to evaluate the expression 8 + 3 + 3, there are two possible methods of determining the value. Either start by adding the first two numbers or start by adding the last two numbers.

Method One		Method Two	
8 + 3 + 3	Add 8 and 3	8 + 3 + 3	Add 3 and 3
11 + 3	Then add 3	8 + 6	Then add 8

a. Do both methods give the same result? Explain below.

b. Use the methods above to evaluate the following expressions.

Method One	Method Two
9 − 4 − 3	9 − 4 − 3

Method One	Method Two
4 × 2 × 3	4 × 2 × 3

Method One	Method Two
16 ÷ 2 ÷ 2	16 ÷ 2 ÷ 2

c. For which operations — addition, subtraction, multiplication, and/or division — do both methods give the same result?

In Question 3, you should have noticed that only the operations of addition and multiplication give the same result when using Method One and Method Two to evaluate the given expressions. The operations of addition and multiplication have special properties that subtraction and division do not have. To be consistent, mathematicians have agreed upon a correct method of evaluating an expression involving one operation and more than one term. They have agreed to evaluate such expressions from left to right, as was done in Method One.

4. Correctly evaluate each expression by working from left to right.

   a. $36 \div 6 \div 2$

   b. $6 + 2 + 4 + 8$

   c. $8 \times 2 \times 4$

   d. $18 - 12 - 4 - 2$

5. Which of the expressions in Question 4 could be evaluated in a different order and still give the correct result?

6. Expressions such as $8 + 2 \times 3$ involve more than one operation.

   a. To find the value of $8 + 2 \times 3$ you might proceed in two ways.

Method One		Method Two	
$8 + 2 \times 3$	Multiply 2 and 3	$8 + 2 \times 3$	Add 8 and 2
$8 + 6$	Add 8	10×3	Multiply by 3

   Is there a problem with accepting both methods as a correct way to evaluate $8 + 2 \times 3$? Explain below.

A Fairly Ordered Operation

b. Finding the value of $8+2\times3$ requires two mathematical operations: addition and multiplication. Mathematicians have agreed that when evaluating an expression containing both addition and multiplication, the operations of addition and multiplication should be performed in the same order as shown in Method One. In what order should the operations of addition and multiplication be completed?

7. Recall that the cost of attending the fair and buying two ride tickets can be expressed as $8+3+3$. Explain why $8+3+3$ can also be expressed as $8+2\times3$.

8. The cost of attending the fair and buying six ride tickets can be expressed as $8+3+3+3+3+3+3$, using only the operation of addition.

a. Write an expression involving addition and multiplication that can also be used to find the cost of attending the fair and buying six ride tickets.

b. Explain how to evaluate the expression in Part (a) to find the cost of attending the fair and buying six ride tickets.

c. Find the cost of attending the fair and buying six ride tickets.

A Fairly Ordered Operation

Part II

One attraction at the Pace County Fair is the Fun House. The maximum occupancy of the Fun House is 30 persons.

9. The attendant is keeping count of the number of people in the Fun House. There are 30 persons in the Fun House, then five persons exit. He allows four more persons to enter, then eight persons exit. Complete the boxes to find the number of people in the Fun House at this time.

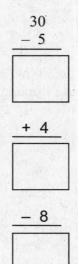

10. The number of people in the Fun House can be expressed as $30 - 5 + 4 - 8$. To evaluate this expression you might proceed in either of two ways.

Method One		Method Two	
$30 - 5 + 4 - 8$	Add 5 and 4	$30 - 5 + 4 - 8$	Subtract 5 from 30
$30 - 9 - 8$	Subtract 9 from 30	$25 + 4 - 8$	Add 25 and 4
$21 - 8$	Subtract 8 from 21	$29 - 8$	Subtract 8 from 29
13		21	

Which one of the two methods results in the correct number of people in the Fun House? Explain your reasoning.

11. To find the value of $30 - 5 + 4 - 8$ requires two mathematical operations: addition and subtraction. Mathematicians have agreed that when evaluating an expression with addition and subtraction, the operations of addition and subtraction should be performed as shown in Method Two. Explain how to evaluate an expression with addition and subtraction.

12. Mathematicians have agreed to evaluate the operations of division and multiplication from left to right before evaluating the operations of addition and subtraction from left to right. Evaluate the expression $15 - 4 + 14 \times 2 - 8 + 15 \div 5$.

Part III

13. To evaluate 2×3^2 you might proceed in one of two ways.

Method One		**Method Two**	
2×3^2	Multiply 2 and 3	2×3^2	Square 3
6^2	Square 6	2×9	Multiply 2 and 9

Do both methods give the same result? Explain below.

14. Finding the value of 2×3^2 requires multiplication and evaluating a power. Mathematicians have agreed that when evaluating such expressions the order in which the multiplication and the evaluating of the power should be completed is the same as shown in Method Two. Explain how to evaluate an expression with multiplication and exponents.

One game at the Pace County Fair involves throwing two darts at a target like the one shown below. The numbers on the target represent the score for one dart landing in each region.

15. How many points will you receive for one dart that lands in the striped region of the target?

16. What is the total number of points that you will receive if both darts land in the striped region of the target?

17. You could express the total number of points that you will receive if both darts land in the striped region of the target as $3^2 + 3^2$.

   a. Rewrite $3^2 + 3^2$ as an expression that uses multiplication rather than addition.

   b. Explain how to correctly evaluate the expression 2×3^2 and compare the result to your answer in Question 16.

18. The total score for both darts landing in the center region of the target can be expressed as $3^3 + 3^3$.

   a. Rewrite $3^3 + 3^3$ as an expression that uses multiplication rather than addition.

   b. Explain how to evaluate the expression 2×3^3.

   c. Find the total score for both darts if they land in the center region of the target.

A Fairly Ordered Operation

Part IV

One food concession at the Pace County Fair offers value meals in addition to à la carte items. An excerpt from the menu is shown below.

À LA CARTE

Corn Dogs ....$3.00   Cotton Candy $2.00
Fried Vegetables ....$5.00   Funnel Cakes $4.00
Iced Tea ....$2.00   Potato Fries $2.50

VALUE MEALS

Corn Dog, Fries, Drink...$6.00   Hamburger, Chips, Drink....$8.00

---

19. Find the cost of buying three orders of cotton candy and one iced tea.

20. If you evaluate the expression $3+1\times2$ in the order that mathematicians have agreed upon, will this expression give the same cost of buying three orders of cotton candy and one iced tea as you found in Question 19? Explain below.

21. To change the order in which the expression $3+1\times2$ is evaluated, parentheses can be placed around the numbers and operation to be performed first. Add parentheses to the expression $3+1\times2$ so that it can be evaluated in such a way as to give the cost of buying three orders of cotton candy and one iced tea as you found in Question 19.

A Fairly Ordered Operation

22. Mathematicians have agreed that in evaluating an expression involving grouping symbols, such as parentheses or brackets, the operations inside the grouping symbols should be completed before completing those operations outside of the grouping symbols. Suppose that a family has ordered one hamburger value meal, four cotton candies, two iced teas, and two corn dog value meals. The total cost of the family's meal can be expressed as $8+(4+2)\times 2+2\times 6$. Find the total cost of the family's meal. Show your work.

23. Consider the expression $6\left[3+2(4+5)\right]$. There are four necessary steps to evaluate this expression. Evaluate this expression showing each of the four steps.

24. Since each numerical expression should have a unique value, mathematicians have agreed upon the order for evaluating each operation. Complete the list below, showing the accepted order of operations.

Step 1:   Evaluate all expressions in _____.

Step 2:   Evaluate all expressions involving _____.

Step 3:   Complete all _____and

_____ from left to right.

Step 4:   Complete all _____and

_____ from left to right.

A Fairly Ordered Operation

25. Describe the correct order of evaluating the expression $20 \div 2^2 + 5 \times 6 - 7$ and then find the value of the expression.

26. Consider the expression $6\left[24/3 + 2 \times \left(17 - 3^2\right)\right]$. There are six necessary steps to evaluate this expression. Evaluate this expression showing each of the six steps.

A Fairly Ordered Operation

Title of Model Instructional Unit: A Fairly Ordered Operation

Embedded Assessment Question # _____   Page # _____

How could you improve your response to this question?

What part of this Model Instructional Unit is an example of your best work? Explain why you feel this is your best work.

What mathematical skills, strategies, or knowledge that you had prior to starting this Model Instructional Unit helped you to complete this activity?

What new mathematical skills, strategies, or knowledge did you obtain while completing this Model Instructional Unit?

Middle School Mathematics I

Analyzing Elections

Contents

Analyzing Elections

Part I

The student council at Metropolis Middle School has requested that each homeroom elect a representative. Mr. Fare's homeroom is made up of students who are all new to the school. He has decided that since the students do not yet know each other, a class election would not make sense. Instead, he has asked interested students to volunteer for the position of homeroom representative. From his homeroom, Andy, Betty, Chenetta, and Deon volunteer for the position. To replace the election process, each of the 23 students in the homeroom will roll a number cube to simulate their vote.

Each student will take a turn rolling the number cube. Rolling a 1 is a vote for Andy, rolling a 2 is a vote for Betty, rolling a 3 is a vote for Chenetta, and rolling a 4 is a vote for Deon. A roll of 5 or 6 is disregarded and the student continues to roll until they roll a number 1 through 4.

1. Answer the following questions.

    a. In your group, roll the number cube until you reach 23 votes. Use the table below to organize your data.

Andy (1)	Betty (2)	Chenetta (3)	Deon (4)	Total Number of Votes

    b. Who will be the homeroom representative?

2. List the names of the candidates in order of most number of votes to least number of votes. Next to his or her name, write the number of votes each candidate received.

3. What fraction of the total votes did each candidate receive?

4. Write the fractions from Question 3 in order, from greatest to least.

Part II

5. In the actual election in Mr. Fare's homeroom, Andy received $\frac{5}{23}$ of the total votes, Betty received $\frac{7}{23}$ of the total votes, Chenetta received $\frac{8}{23}$ of the total votes, and Deon received $\frac{3}{23}$ of the total votes. Who is the homeroom representative?

6. At Metropolis Middle School, there was a traditional election held for student council officers. Eden, Frank, Gabrielle, and Hernando were candidates for president. Three hundred students voted. Eden received $\frac{4}{15}$ of the votes, Frank received $\frac{3}{10}$ of the votes, Gabrielle received $\frac{1}{30}$ of the votes, and Hernando received $\frac{2}{5}$ of the votes. Why is it more difficult to determine the winner of this election than the winner of the election in Question 5?

7. One way to make it easier to compare the results from the student council presidential election is to find how many of the 300 votes each candidate received. Below, change each of the fractions in Question 6 to a fraction with a denominator of 300.

8. Answer the following questions.

    a. Why did changing each fraction to an equivalent fraction with a denominator of 300 make it easier to compare the fractions of the total number of votes each candidate received?

    b. List other common denominators that could be used to compare the fractions from the presidential election results at Metropolis Middle School.

    c. Would one of the common denominators that you listed in Part (b) be easier to work with than 300 to compare the fractions? Explain why or why not.

    d. Change each fraction in Question 6 to an equivalent fraction with the denominator you chose in Part (c).

9. One technique for organizing large amounts of information is to make a table. Complete the table below.

Candidate	Fraction of Votes	Fraction with Denominator of 300	Fraction with Denominator of Your Choice	Final Rank in Election (1st – 4th Place)
Eden	$\frac{4}{15}$			
Frank	$\frac{3}{10}$			
Gabrielle	$\frac{1}{30}$			
Hernando	$\frac{2}{5}$			

10. Order the fractions below, from largest to smallest.

$$\frac{4}{15} \qquad \frac{3}{10} \qquad \frac{1}{30} \qquad \frac{2}{5}$$

11. Order the fractions below, from largest to smallest. Show your work.

$$\frac{5}{8} \qquad \frac{3}{4} \qquad \frac{2}{3} \qquad \frac{1}{6}$$

12. Order the fractions below, from smallest to largest. Show your work.

$$\frac{7}{15} \qquad \frac{2}{5} \qquad \frac{4}{9} \qquad \frac{10}{45}$$

Analyzing Elections

Part III

Hernando is the recently elected student council president at Metropolis Middle School. As president, he realizes that he should speak with each of the student groups in his school to find out what issues are important to them. Hernando gets the following data from the guidance counselor:

- $\frac{8}{15}$ of the students participate in music

- $\frac{1}{6}$ of the students participate in the art club

- $\frac{16}{33}$ of the students participate in sports

- $\frac{4}{9}$ of the students participate in academic clubs

Hernando decides that he should speak with the groups with the most participants first, and to do this he must reorder the fractions. He realizes that the common denominator for these fractions would be very large, so he asks his math teacher, Mr. Fare, if there is an easier way to reorder the fractions. Mr. Fare decides to use less complicated fractions in his explanation.

13. Answer the following.

    a. Help Hernando to represent each of the fractions below by shading in the appropriate amount of each rectangle below.

    b. Use the diagrams to reorder the fractions $\frac{1}{3}$, $\frac{1}{4}$, $\frac{1}{2}$, and $\frac{1}{5}$, from greatest to least.

    c. Each of the fractions above has the same numerator. Explain how Hernando can use the denominators to reorder the fractions.

d. Using the method you described in Part (c), reorder the fractions $\frac{4}{5}$, $\frac{4}{11}$, $\frac{4}{7}$, and $\frac{4}{25}$, from greatest to least.

14. Hernando realizes that the fractions given to him by the guidance counselor do not have a common numerator. He thinks that for these fractions, it will be easier to get a common numerator rather than a common denominator. Answer the following.

    a. What is the least common numerator of the fractions $\frac{8}{15}$, $\frac{1}{6}$, $\frac{16}{33}$, and $\frac{4}{9}$?

    b. Change each of the fractions above to the equivalent fraction with the common numerator found in Part (a).

    c. Order the fractions in Part (b) from greatest to least.

    d. In what order should Hernando talk with the student groups?

Analyzing Elections

Part IV

Here are the results from the 1860 U.S. presidential election:

- Stephen A. Douglas received $\dfrac{1,382,713}{4,689,568}$ of the total votes.

- John C. Breckinridge received $\dfrac{212,089}{1,172,392}$ of the total votes.

- Abraham Lincoln received $\dfrac{1,865,593}{4,689,568}$ of the total votes.

- John Bell received $\dfrac{296,453}{2,344,784}$ of the total votes.

15. Use a calculator to help answer this question. List the order, from most to fewest votes, in which the candidates placed in the 1860 presidential election. Show work or explain how you arrived at your answer.

Analyzing Elections

Title of Model Instructional Unit: Analyzing Elections

Embedded Assessment Question # _____ Page # _____

How could you improve your response to this question?

What part of this Model Instructional Unit is an example of your best work? Explain why you feel this is your best work.

What mathematical skills, strategies, or knowledge that you had prior to starting this Model Instructional Unit helped you to complete this activity?

What new mathematical skills, strategies, or knowledge did you obtain while completing this Model Instructional Unit?

Middle School Mathematics I
Designing the Stage Set

Contents

Part I

Selene and Gregg are constructing a stage set for the school play. They are creating a living room scene and need some fabric to make drapes and pillows for the couch and chair, and to cover a lamp shade and other decorative accessories. Gregg found a piece of fabric on sale that he thought would look good on the set. The fabric came in a width that would be easy to work with for constructing the stage set. All Gregg needed to know was the length of the fabric. He measured the length of the fabric and it was $6\frac{3}{4}$ feet long. He determined that the drapes require $3\frac{1}{3}$ feet of fabric; the pillows require $2\frac{1}{2}$ feet of fabric; and the lamp shade and decorative accessories require $1\frac{1}{4}$ feet of fabric. Gregg asked Selene to determine if there is enough fabric to complete the set. Work through the questions below to help Selene answer Gregg's question.

1. Selene looks at Gregg's measurements and quickly determines that she needs at least 6 feet of fabric by adding the whole number parts of each measurement. She is concerned about the additional $\frac{1}{3}$ foot, $\frac{1}{2}$ foot, and $\frac{1}{4}$ foot lengths of fabric.

   a. There are 12 inches in 1 foot. Complete the table below.

Size	Number of Inches
$\frac{1}{4}$ foot	
$\frac{1}{3}$ foot	
$\frac{1}{2}$ foot	
$\frac{2}{3}$ foot	
$\frac{3}{4}$ foot	
1 foot	12

b. Use the table in Part (a) to determine the total number of inches of fabric that will be required to supply the $\frac{1}{3}$ foot, $\frac{1}{2}$ foot, and $\frac{1}{4}$ foot pieces.

2. Is the total number of inches that you found in Question 1 for the additional $\frac{1}{3}$, $\frac{1}{2}$, and $\frac{1}{4}$ feet of fabric *more* than 1 foot of fabric or *less* than 1 foot of fabric? Explain how you arrived at this answer.

3. Rewrite the fractions in the table below as equivalent fractions with a denominator of 12. You may want to refer to the table in Question 1.

Size	Measure in 12ths of a Foot
$\frac{1}{4}$ foot	
$\frac{1}{3}$ foot	
$\frac{1}{2}$ foot	
$\frac{2}{3}$ foot	
$\frac{3}{4}$ foot	
1 foot	$\frac{12}{12}$

4. The following sum represents the total amount of fabric needed for the stage set items:

$$3\frac{1}{3} \text{ feet } + 2\frac{1}{2} \text{ feet } + 1\frac{1}{4}\text{feet}$$

a. Use the information in Question 3 to rewrite $1\frac{1}{4}$ feet in terms of 12ths of a foot.

b. Use the information in Question 3 to rewrite each term in the sum $3\frac{1}{3}$ feet $+ 2\frac{1}{2}$ feet $+ 1\frac{1}{4}$ feet in terms of 12ths of a foot.

c. How does this sum relate to your work in Question 3?

5. Do Gregg and Selene have enough fabric to make all three stage set items?

Part II

In mathematics, when two or more objects can be combined under the operation of addition we call them **like terms**. For example, 3 apples + 4 apples = 7 apples, because apple is the common or like object in both terms of the sum and the terms can be combined to give the sum seven apples. Addition and subtraction of fractions is similar to this idea.

6. A teacher cut a candy bar into eight *exactly* equal pieces. One student received two of the pieces and his friend received three of the pieces.

    a. Use the candy bar illustration below to indicate eight equal pieces.

    b. Shade in the two pieces the first student received and the three pieces his friend received and write each as a fraction of the candy bar.

    c. Write a sum of fractions that indicates the combined amount of the candy bar that the student and his friend received.

    d. Write the sum in Part (c) as a single fraction representing the combined total.

    e. The expressions in Parts (c) and (d) look different but they are numerically equal. Explain why they are equal even though they appear different.

7. This teacher also baked several recipes of brownies. He made each recipe in an 8-inch × 8-inch pan and cut brownies that were exactly 2 inches × 2 inches.

    a. Draw a square to represent the 8-inch × 8-inch pan, then illustrate the brownies in this pan.

    b. How many brownies did the teacher make in each pan?

    c. What fractional part of a whole recipe is one brownie?

    d. In one of the brownie pans the teacher forgot to cut the last piece. This left a 2-inch × 4-inch brownie. Greedy Gus took that piece and one of the 2-inch × 2-inch brownies. What part of the pan of brownies did Greedy Gus take?

In Question 6, we saw that the sum $\frac{2}{8}+\frac{3}{8}$ has meaning as a sum, but that it also can be expressed as a single fraction; namely, $\frac{2}{8}+\frac{3}{8}=\frac{5}{8}$. The single fraction answer for the sum $\frac{2}{8}+\frac{3}{8}$ was possible because we were adding together a common fractional unit. The common fractional unit was $\frac{1}{8}$. Thus, the sum $\frac{2}{8}+\frac{3}{8}$ can be thought of as adding two of the $\frac{1}{8}$ pieces of the candy bar plus three of the $\frac{1}{8}$ pieces of the candy bar for a total of five of the $\frac{1}{8}$ pieces of the candy bar. Another way of viewing this sum is to think of $\frac{2}{8}+\frac{3}{8}$ as $2\times\frac{1}{8}+3\times\frac{1}{8}$. This means that the sum is $2 + 3$ of the $\frac{1}{8}$ pieces of the candy bar, which can be written as $\frac{5}{8}$ of the candy bar.

Therefore, fractions with the same denominator can be added because they have the same common fractional unit, and since addition combines "like" objects, these fractions can be added by combining their numerators.

8. For each problem below, identify the common fractional unit and then perform the arithmetic operation that expresses the sum (difference) as a single fraction.

    a. $\frac{1}{6}+\frac{4}{6}$

    b. $\frac{2}{5}+\frac{3}{5}$

    c. $\frac{5}{11}+\frac{3}{11}$

Part III

In Part II, you learned how addition and subtraction of fractions worked when there was a common fractional unit because the fractional units were like terms. It was the same idea as 3 apples + 4 apples = 7 apples. While it may seem strange to want to add 3 apples + 2 oranges, imagine a fruit basket containing three apples and two oranges. The sum of 3 apples + 2 oranges is a sum that represents the contents of the fruit basket, but these cannot be combined into a single number because apples and oranges are two different kinds of fruit. But the sum of 3 apples + 2 oranges does have meaning when describing the total amount of fruit in the basket.

If fractions do not have the same denominator, they must be expressed in terms of a common fractional unit before they can be added together. The following activities are designed to help with the understanding that fractions can have different numerical representations yet be equal to the same quantity.

9. The teacher asks his students to work with two identical candy bars.

Candy Bar 1

Candy Bar 2

a. On Candy Bar 1, shade in the meaning of $\frac{1}{4}$ of the candy bar.

b. On Candy Bar 2, shade in the meaning of $\frac{1}{3}$ of the candy bar.

c. Use your drawings from above to draw a picture below of the meaning of $\frac{1}{4} + \frac{1}{3}$ of a candy bar.

10. The fraction sum $\frac{1}{4} + \frac{1}{3}$ cannot be combined unless a common fractional unit is found that allows us to express each fraction of the sum in terms of this common fractional unit.

   a. Use the illustration of the candy bar shown below to shade in the fraction $\frac{1}{4}$.

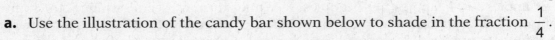

   b. Use the illustration of the candy bar shown below to shade in the fraction $\frac{1}{3}$.

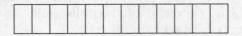

   c. What is the basic fractional unit in the two illustrations shown above for the candy bar? Explain how you determined this fractional unit.

   d. Use the fractional unit in Part (c) to express $\frac{1}{4}$ as another equivalent fraction.

   e. Use the fractional unit in Part (c) to express $\frac{1}{3}$ as another equivalent fraction.

   f. Based on your observations in the previous parts of this question, what is the sum $\frac{1}{4} + \frac{1}{3}$ expressed as a single fraction of the candy bar?

11. Below is an illustration of the candy bar divided into four equal parts.

    a. Divide each of the four parts of the candy bar into two equal parts. Give the fractional unit that represents the new parts into which the candy bar has been divided.

    b. Explain, in words, how $\frac{1}{2} \cdot \frac{1}{4}$ is a mathematical expression using fractions that describes Part (a).

    c. Use the candy bar drawing above to explain why the numerical equation $\frac{1}{2} \cdot \frac{1}{4} = \frac{1}{8}$ is true.

    d. Express the fraction $\frac{1}{4}$ as an equivalent fraction in the new fractional unit from Part (a).

12. Below is an illustration of the candy bar divided into four equal parts.

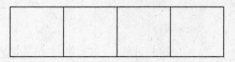

    a. Divide each part of the above candy bar into three equal parts. Give the fractional unit that represents the new parts into which the candy bar has been divided.

    b. Explain, in words, how $\frac{1}{3} \cdot \frac{1}{4}$ is a mathematical expression using fractions that describes Part (a).

    c. Use the candy bar drawing to explain why the numerical equation $\frac{1}{3} \cdot \frac{1}{4} = \frac{1}{12}$ is true.

    d. Express the fraction $\frac{1}{4}$ as an equivalent fraction in the new fractional unit from Part (a).

13. Your work in Questions 11 and 12 illustrates a process that can be used for finding equivalent fractions for the fraction $\frac{1}{4}$.

   a. List another fraction that is equivalent to the fraction $\frac{1}{4}$.

   b. Explain the process that you used to arrive at your fraction in Part (a).

   c. Use the candy bar picture below to illustrate and explain why the new fraction is actually mathematically equivalent to the fraction $\frac{1}{4}$.

   d. Give an explanation that requires no picture for why the new fraction is actually equal to the fraction $\frac{1}{4}$.

Designing the Stage Set

Take five strips of different colored paper, all of the same length. Fold one strip into halves, one into thirds, one into fourths, and one into sixths. (To form sixths, fold the paper into thirds, then fold each third in half.) Leave one strip unfolded to represent the number one.

14. Match up the strips to help rename the fractions. Draw a sketch of your strips and complete the fraction for each problem below.

     a. $\dfrac{1}{3} = \dfrac{}{6}$

     b. $\dfrac{1}{2} = \dfrac{}{6}$

     c. $\dfrac{1}{2} = \dfrac{}{4}$

     d. $\dfrac{4}{4} = \dfrac{}{6} = \dfrac{}{3} = \dfrac{}{2} = 1$

     e. How did you arrive at your answer in Part (d)?

Part IV

The previous questions have illustrated an important property of fractions; namely, the **Property of One**. The Property of One for fractions states that if the numerator and the denominator of a fraction are multiplied by the same number its value is not changed. The reason this property is called the Property of One is because multiplying a fraction by $\frac{2}{2}$, $\frac{3}{3}$, or $\frac{4}{4}$ is the same as multiplying the fraction by the number one. Each of the fractions, $\frac{2}{2}$, $\frac{3}{3}$, or $\frac{4}{4}$ describe the number one in different ways. For example, the fraction $\frac{1}{2}$ is equivalent to $\frac{3}{6}$ because $\frac{1}{2} = \frac{1}{2} \times 1 = \frac{1}{2} \times \frac{3}{3} = \frac{1 \times 3}{2 \times 3} = \frac{3}{6}$. Here, the numerator and denominator are each multiplied by three. It can also be understood that the fractions have the same value because the fraction $\frac{1}{2}$ refers to one of the two parts that the object is cut or folded into and the fraction $\frac{3}{6}$ refers to three of the six parts that the object is cut or folded into.

As another illustration of the Property of One, the fraction $\frac{2}{3}$ is equivalent to the fraction $\frac{6}{9}$ because $\frac{2}{3} = \frac{2}{3} \times 1 = \frac{2}{3} \times \frac{3}{3} = \frac{6}{9}$.

15. Use the method described above to rename the fractions below.

    a. $\frac{1}{2} = \frac{}{10}$

    b. $\frac{3}{5} = \frac{6}{}$

    c. $\frac{15}{25} = \frac{}{5}$

16. Find a common denominator for the fractions in each sum below and then add or subtract the fractions as indicated.

    a. $\dfrac{2}{3} + \dfrac{3}{4}$

    b. $\dfrac{1}{2} - \dfrac{1}{5}$

    c. $\dfrac{1}{5} + \dfrac{1}{2} - \dfrac{1}{3}$

Use the methods you learned in the previous parts to answer the following question.

17. Cindy bought $4\dfrac{2}{3}$ yards of fabric for her costume for the play but only used $2\dfrac{1}{4}$ yards. How much fabric does Cindy have remaining? Show your work.

Designing the Stage Set

Title of Model Instructional Unit: Designing the Stage Set

Embedded Assessment Question # _____ Page # _____

How could you improve your response to this question?

What part of this Model Instructional Unit is an example of your best work? Explain why you feel this is your best work.

What mathematical skills, strategies, or knowledge that you had prior to starting this Model Instructional Unit helped you to complete this activity?

What new mathematical skills, strategies, or knowledge did you obtain while completing this Model Instructional Unit?

Middle School Mathematics I
Cooking with André

Contents

Cooking with André

Part I

1. You have been asked to make coffee cake for a school party, using a recipe that calls for the following ingredients:

    2 cups sifted flour

    2 eggs

    1 cup sugar

    1 cup sour cream

    1 teaspoon vanilla

    1 teaspoon baking soda

    1 teaspoon ground cinnamon

    $1\frac{1}{2}$ teaspoons baking powder

    $\frac{1}{2}$ cup butter

    $\frac{1}{4}$ teaspoon salt

    The recipe you have was intended to feed five persons, but you need to prepare enough for all 60 students in your grade.

    a. How would you adjust the recipe to feed 60 students?

    b. List all of the ingredient amounts needed for the adjusted recipe.

2. Your friend Kashi knows an alternate recipe for coffee cake (also meant to feed five persons) that includes raisins. When Kashi rescales his recipe to feed 60, his recipe calls for "18 cups of raisins."

    a. How many cups of raisins does Kashi's original recipe require? Write a number sentence to find the answer.

    b. Draw a picture below to illustrate this calculation.

3. Your classmates Liz and Jean are making cookies for the same party. Their original cookie recipe calls for 2 cups of flour but instead they will use 14 cups of flour.

    a. How many batches of cookies will Liz and Jean make? Write a number sentence to find the answer.

    b. Draw a picture below to illustrate this calculation.

Cooking with André

4. Kashi asks for your help in preparing a squash casserole for dinner at his home. Unfortunately, the only recipe he has for this dish comes from his uncle's old army cookbook, which was written for cooks preparing food for 200 people at a time. Kashi asks you to adjust the recipe to make enough casserole for five persons. The ingredients list reads as follows:

240 zucchini, sliced

80 eggs, beaten

40 cups mayonnaise

40 cups grated cheddar cheese

1000 crackers, crushed

10 teaspoons ground black pepper

60 small onions, diced

80 tablespoons butter

a. How much of each ingredient does Kashi need to cook the squash casserole for five persons? Show your work.

b. Can you solve the problem another way? If so, show that method.

Part II

After helping Kashi, you decide to enroll in a summer cooking class at a local community college taught by a chef named André. André is an excellent cook but a little disorganized. As a result, you are never quite sure if you have enough of the right ingredients on your table at the beginning of class.

(Your teacher will provide you with measuring cups and spoons, along with something to measure – such as rice – to help with answering these questions.)

5. On the first day of class, expecting that you will make a multi-layered cake, you measure 6 cups of flour before class begins. When André comes by, he says, "That's too much flour! You only need 2 cups of flour for this recipe."

a. Draw 6 cups of flour below. According to André, the recipe calls for 2 cups of flour per batch. Use your drawing to indicate how many batches 6 cups of flour will yield.

b. Your drawing should indicate that 6 cups of flour have been separated into 2 cups per batch. The same process indicated in your drawing can be indicated with arithmetic. Complete the following arithmetic equation to represent the process of separating cups of flour into recipe batches that is shown by your drawing in Part (a).

6 cups of flour ÷ _____ cups per batch = _____ batches

c. What arithmetic operation modeled the separation process used in your drawing to find the number of recipe batches in 6 cups of flour?

d. Suppose that another recipe required 3 cups of flour per batch. Write an arithmetic equation using units attached to each number in your equation that indicates the number of batches there are in 6 cups of flour. Use the arithmetic equation in Part (b) as a model.

6. On the second day of class, you measure 2 teaspoons of baking powder before class begins. When André comes by, he says, "That's too much baking powder! You only need $\frac{1}{2}$ teaspoon for this recipe!"

a. Measure 2 teaspoons of baking powder onto your table. Separate the baking powder into $\frac{1}{2}$-teaspoon piles. How many piles do you have?

b. Draw a picture below that represents this situation.

c. How many batches of the recipe can you make with the 2 teaspoons of baking powder? Explain below.

d. Express your answer to Part (c) by completing the following arithmetic equation.

2 teaspoons of baking powder $\div$ $\frac{1}{2}$ teaspoon per batch = _____ batches

7. On the third day of class, you measure 3 cups of flour. When class begins, André announces, "Today's recipe calls for $\frac{3}{4}$ cup of flour."

a. Measure 3 cups of flour onto your table. Separate the flour into $\frac{1}{4}$-cup piles. How many piles do you have?

b. Draw a picture below that represents this situation.

c. Express your answer to Part (a) by completing the following arithmetic equation.

3 cups of flour ÷ $\frac{1}{4}$ cup of flour per pile = _____ piles

d. How many $\frac{1}{4}$-cup piles of flour are there in 1 cup of flour?

e. Complete the following arithmetic equation and explain why it makes sense.

3 cups of flour × _____ piles per cup of flour = _____ piles

f. How many of the $\frac{1}{4}$-cup piles of flour in Part (c) are needed to make one recipe batch? Explain below.

g. Complete the following arithmetic equation that describes the number of recipe batches in 3 cups of flour.

_____ piles ÷ _____ piles per batch = _____ batches

h. The answer to Part (c) can also be expressed by the following arithmetic equation. Complete the following equation and explain why it also gives the answer to the number of recipe batches in 3 cups of flour.

3 cups of flour ÷ $\dfrac{3}{4}$ cup of flour per batch = _____ batches

i. Which of the previous parts of this question indicate that the following arithmetic equation makes sense? Be certain to use units in your explanation.

$$3 \div \frac{1}{4} = 3 \times 4$$

j. Which of the previous parts of this question indicate that the following arithmetic equation makes sense? Be certain to use units in your explanation.

$$3 \div \frac{3}{4} = \frac{3}{1} \times \frac{4}{3}$$

8. If the fourth day's recipe calls for $\frac{2}{3}$ cup of flour, how many batches of the recipe could you make with 4 cups of flour?

   a. Measure 4 cups of flour onto your table. Separate the flour into $\frac{1}{3}$-cup piles. How many piles do you have?

   b. Draw a picture below that represents this situation.

   c. Write an arithmetic equation, similar to your work in Question 7, that indicates the answer to Part (a). Be certain to use units for each number in your equation.

   d. How many $\frac{1}{3}$-cup piles of flour are there in 1 cup of flour?

   e. Complete the following arithmetic equation and explain why it makes sense.

   4 cups of flour × _____ piles per cup of flour = _____ piles

Cooking with André

f. How many of the piles of flour in Part (a) are needed to make one recipe batch? Explain below.

g. Complete the following arithmetic equation that describes the number of recipe batches in 4 cups of flour.

_____ piles ÷ _____ piles per batch = _____ batches

h. Complete the following equation and explain why it also gives the answer to the number of recipe batches in 4 cups of flour.

4 cups of flour ÷ $\dfrac{2}{3}$ cup of flour per batch = _____ batches

i. Which of the previous parts of this question indicate that the following arithmetic equation makes sense? Be certain to use units in your explanation.

$$4 \div \frac{1}{3} = 4 \times 3$$

j. Which of the previous parts of this question indicate that the following arithmetic equation makes sense? Be certain to use units in your explanation.

$$4 \div \frac{2}{3} = \frac{4}{1} \times \frac{3}{2}$$

Cooking with André

STUDENT ACTIVITY (continued)

Part III

In Part II, we modeled what happens when a number is divided by a fraction. Using the modeling activities, you have discovered that division by a fraction is equivalent to multiplying the dividend (the first number in a division expression) by the reciprocal of the divisor (the second number in the division expression). For example:

$$3 \div \frac{3}{4} = \frac{3}{1} \times \frac{4}{3} \text{ or } 4 \div \frac{2}{3} = \frac{4}{1} \times \frac{3}{2}.$$

9. It is the final day of your cooking class, and you are expecting André's last-minute corrections. Today your cooking station has 4 teaspoons of baking powder measured in front of it. When André comes by, he announces, "Today's special recipe calls for $\frac{3}{5}$ of a teaspoon of baking powder per batch!"

   a. Write an arithmetic expression using division and appropriate units for the numbers to give the number of recipe batches in 4 teaspoons of baking powder if each batch requires $\frac{3}{5}$ teaspoon of baking powder.

   b. Write an arithmetic expression using multiplication and appropriate units for the numbers to give the number of recipe batches in 4 teaspoons of baking powder.

10. After graduating from André's cooking class, you decide to try a recipe from your family cookbook. You have 12 teaspoons of baking powder and the recipe calls for $\frac{3}{4}$ teaspoon of baking powder. How many batches will you be able to make with the 12 teaspoons of baking powder? Write an arithmetic expression using division and appropriate units for the numbers to give the number of recipe batches in 12 teaspoons of baking powder if each batch requires $\frac{3}{4}$ teaspoon of baking powder.

Then use what you know about division of fractions to answer the question.

Cooking with André

Title of Model Instructional Unit: Cooking with André

Embedded Assessment Question # _____   Page # _____

How could you improve your response to this question?

What part of this Model Instructional Unit is an example of your best work? Explain why you feel this is your best work.

What mathematical skills, strategies, or knowledge that you had prior to starting this Model Instructional Unit helped you to complete this activity?

What new mathematical skills, strategies, or knowledge did you obtain while completing this Model Instructional Unit?

Middle School Mathematics I

Integer Games

Contents

Integer Games

Part I *Opposites Attract*

Rules for *Opposites Attract*
(4 Players)

Materials
- *Integer Game*s deck of cards

Playing the Game
- One player deals seven cards to each player.
- Turn the rest of the cards facedown and turn the top card from the deck over to begin the discard pile.
- Starting with the player to the left of the dealer, each player takes one card, lays down any sets of cards they have in their hand, and discards one card.
- Play continues in a clockwise direction.
- The game ends as soon as a player has no cards remaining in his or her hand after discarding.

Laying Down a Set
- Each card has a number and a sign. A player must have *one* of the following combinations in order to lay down a set:
  - One negative card and one positive card with the same numerical value
  - Two positive cards that sum to the numerical value of a negative card *and* that negative card
  - Two negative cards that sum to the numerical value of a positive card *and* that positive card

  For example, a player may lay down the set of a positive 3, a positive 5, and a negative 8.

Taking a Card
- Before a player puts down any sets from their hand, they must take a card from the top of the facedown pile or take a card from the discard pile.

Discarding
- Each player must discard one card onto the discard pile at the end of his or her turn.

Winning the Game
- At the end of each round, players receive one point for every card that they have put down in front of them. They must subtract one point for every card left in their hand. The player with the most points wins.

Integer Games

1. Play two rounds of *Opposites Attract*. Record your results below and find your score.

Cards in Each Set You Made	Cards Remaining in Your Hand	Points Added	Points Subtracted	Score

2. Which member of your group won each round?

3. Within your group, discuss the strategies that were used during the game. Which strategies helped players to win each round?

Integer Games

Laying down sets of cards is very similar to the way positive and negative numbers are added. The positive cards represent positive integers (+1, +2, +3, +4, …), and negative cards represent negative integers (–1, –2, –3, –4, …). Cards form a set only when their sum is zero.

4. During one round, Dylan placed a –8 and a +8 on the table. Express this as a number sentence showing two integers whose sum is zero.

5. During the same round, Donovan placed a +5, a –3, and a –2 on the table. Express this as a number sentence showing three integers whose sum is zero.

6. Why do you think this game is called *Opposites Attract*?

7. Look back at the sets you made in Question 1 and record each set below, as a number sentence whose sum is zero.

8. In Question 5, Donovan used a –3 and a –2 in place of a –5. Express this as a number sentence below, showing two negative integers whose sum is equal to another negative integer.

9. Dionne has a –4 and a –2 in her hand.

    a. What card could be used in place of these cards?

    b. Express this as a number sentence below, showing two negative integers whose sum is equal to another negative integer.

    c. Dionne also has a –8 in her hand. Write a new number sentence below, showing three negative integers whose sum is equal to –8.

10. Now try a variation of *Opposites Attract*. Play the game again. This time there is no limit to the number of cards that a player can use to form a set. For example, a player could lay down a set formed by a +2, a +7, a –5, a –3, and a –1. In each set, the total face value of the negative card(s) must equal the total face value of the positive card(s). Record your results below.

Cards in Each Set You Made	Cards Remaining in Your Hand	Points Added	Points Subtracted	Score

11. The sum of two or more integers will always be positive, negative, or zero. Describe the following sums as positive, negative, or zero, and write a number sentence that illustrates each statement below.

   a. The sum of a number and its opposite.

   b. The sum of two or more positive integers.

   c. The sum of two or more negative integers.

   d. The sum of a positive integer and a negative integer.

Integer Games

STUDENT ACTIVITY (continued)

Part II *Get to Zero*

12. Here is a scorecard for a new game called *Get to Zero*. Your teacher is going to help you learn to play this game.

Get to Zero Scorecard

Player	1st Card	Chip	2nd Card	Markers in the Player's Pile	Result
Jonas	+5	Add	–1		
Amy	–3	Subtract	–2		
Mike	+4	Add	+3		
Maria	–3	Subtract	–5		
Gabe	–5	Subtract	+7		

13. The winner is the person whose result is closest to zero. Who won the game?

14. Write a number sentence for each player below. Jonas' number sentence is done for you.

a. Jonas $\qquad +5 + (-1) = +4$

b. Amy

c. Mike

d. Maria

e. Gabe

Rules of *Get to Zero*
(3 to 5 Players)

Materials
- *Integer Games* deck of cards
- One Add/Subtract chip
- A container of positive markers
- A container of negative markers

Playing the Game
- One player deals one card to each player.
- Each player takes markers from the container to represent the number on their card.
- Starting with the player on the dealer's left, each player tosses the Add/Subtract chip and is dealt a new card by the dealer or the player passes. Play continues in a clockwise direction. Based on the results of flipping the chip and drawing a new card, players add or subtract markers from their pile of markers. If a player passes they do nothing. Their points for the round will be the number of the first card they were dealt.

    - If the chip lands on Add, players take markers from the appropriate container to represent the number on their card and add them to their pile.
    - If the chip lands on Subtract, players remove markers from their pile that represent the number on their card and put the markers in the appropriate container. A "zero pair" of markers may need to be borrowed from the container in order to subtract the number of the card. A "zero pair" is one positive marker and one negative marker.

- After everyone, including the dealer, has had a turn, each player removes any "zero pairs" from their pile and puts those markers in the appropriate container.

Winning the Game
- The player that gets closest to zero (the fewest number of markers) wins.

Integer Games

15. Now play *Get to Zero* in your group several times. Use the scorecard to record your play for each game.

				Get to Zero Scorecard		
Game	**1st Card**	**Chip**	**2nd Card**	**Markers in Your Pile**		**Result**
1						
2						
3						
4						
5						

16. How many games did you win?

17. Write a number sentence for each game that you played. Exchange your scorecard with another member of your group to verify each other's work.

18. Teddy needs help completing his scorecard. Use what you learned in the previous questions to fill in the Result column. In which game did Teddy get closest to zero?

Get to Zero Scorecard for Teddy				
Game	**Markers in Your Pile**			**Result**
	1st Card	**Add/Subtract Chip**	**2nd Card**	
1	−8	Add	−7	
2	+3	Subtract	+7	
3	−6	Subtract	−6	
4	−7	Add	+4	
5	+1	Add	−1	
6	+3	Subtract	−8	

19. Use the numbers from the scorecard in Question 18 to write six number sentences below for each game that Teddy played. The first game has been done for you.

Game 1 $-8 + (-7) = -15$ Game 4 _____

Game 2 _____   Game 5 _____

Game 3 _____   Game 6 _____

20. For the addition problems in Question 19, explain how you can tell if the result is going to be positive or negative before you combine the numbers.

21. In Game 6, Teddy noticed that when he subtracted a negative number, his score went up!

a. Explain why this occurred.

b. Write a rule for subtracting a negative number from another integer.

Integer Games

22. Use what you have learned to complete the following. Use positive and negative markers if needed to model each problem. Explain how you arrived at your answers.

    a. $8 + (-5) =$

    b. $(-5) - 8 =$

    c. $12 - (-2) =$

    d. $3 + (-25) =$

STUDENT ACTIVITY (continued)

Part III Keeping Score

You have been asked to serve as one of the scorekeepers for your school's annual math competition. Each round of the competition consists of five questions. Every contestant earns points for a correct answer. Contestants lose points if they answer incorrectly. Contestants are awarded points based upon the order in which they answer the question correctly as shown below.

- The first person to answer the question correctly earns four points.

- The second person to answer the question correctly earns three points.

- The third person to answer the question correctly earns two points.

- All other contestants who answer the question correctly earn one point.

- Four points are deducted from the score for answering a question incorrectly.

- A contestant may pass on a question and they do not earn or lose any points.

23. Calculate Arthur's results for Round 1 by completing the scorecard below.

Arthur's First Round Results						
Results	**Question Number**					**Total Score for Round 1**
	1	**2**	**3**	**4**	**5**	
	2nd correct answer	4th correct answer	1st correct answer	4th correct answer	incorrect answer	
Point Value						

Integer Games

24. Here are results for all the contestants for Round 1. Find each contestant's score as you did for Arthur in Question 23.

<table>
<tr><td rowspan="3">Contestants</td><td colspan="5">Math Competition
First Round Outcomes</td><td rowspan="3">Total Score
for Round 1</td></tr>
<tr><td colspan="5">Question Number</td></tr>
<tr><td>1</td><td>2</td><td>3</td><td>4</td><td>5</td></tr>
<tr><td rowspan="2">Arthur</td><td>2nd correct answer</td><td>4th correct answer</td><td>1st correct answer</td><td>4th correct answer</td><td>incorrect answer</td><td></td></tr>
<tr><td></td><td></td><td></td><td></td><td></td><td></td></tr>
<tr><td rowspan="2">Bea</td><td>4th correct answer</td><td>2nd correct answer</td><td>2nd correct answer</td><td>2nd correct answer</td><td>2nd correct answer</td><td></td></tr>
<tr><td></td><td></td><td></td><td></td><td></td><td></td></tr>
<tr><td rowspan="2">Charlotte</td><td>1st correct answer</td><td>3rd correct answer</td><td>incorrect answer</td><td>6th correct answer</td><td>incorrect answer</td><td></td></tr>
<tr><td></td><td></td><td></td><td></td><td></td><td></td></tr>
<tr><td rowspan="2">Don</td><td>incorrect answer</td><td>5th correct answer</td><td>incorrect answer</td><td>5th correct answer</td><td>3rd correct answer</td><td></td></tr>
<tr><td></td><td></td><td></td><td></td><td></td><td></td></tr>
<tr><td rowspan="2">Elvis</td><td>incorrect answer</td><td>1st correct answer</td><td>pass</td><td>3rd correct answer</td><td>1st correct answer</td><td></td></tr>
<tr><td></td><td></td><td></td><td></td><td></td><td></td></tr>
<tr><td rowspan="2">Ferdinand</td><td>3rd correct answer</td><td>incorrect answer</td><td>3rd correct answer</td><td>1st correct answer</td><td>incorrect answer</td><td></td></tr>
<tr><td></td><td></td><td></td><td></td><td></td><td></td></tr>
</table>

25. Complete the standings sheet below for Round 1. *Express the points away from first place as a negative number.*

Standings After Round 1			
Place	**Contestant Name**	**Round 1 Score**	**Points Away From First Place**
1st			0
2nd			
3rd			
4th			
5th			
6th			

26. Ferdinand had a total of 0 points after the first round by scoring one first correct answer, two third correct answers, and two incorrect answers. What are some other ways to score 0 points after the first round?

27. Find the highest possible score for one round of the math competition. Explain how you solved this problem.

28. Express the answer to Question 27 as a product of two positive integers. How do each of the integers relate to the math competition?

29. Find the lowest possible score for one round of the math competition using a negative integer. Explain how you solved this problem.

30. Express the answer to Question 29 as a product of a positive integer and a negative integer. How do each of the integers relate to the math competition?

31. In Round 2 of this math competition, Arthur had three first correct answers and two incorrect answers, Bea had two second correct answers and three incorrect answers, and Charlotte had one first correct answer and four passes.

   a. Write an expression that uses multiplication and addition to calculate Arthur's score for Round 2.

   b. Write an expression that uses multiplication and addition to calculate Bea's score for Round 2.

   c. Write an expression that uses multiplication and addition to calculate Charlotte's score for Round 2.

Integer Games

32. The product of two integers will always be positive, negative, or 0. Describe the following products as positive, negative, or 0, and give an example to illustrate each one.

    a. The product of two positive integers.

    b. The product of a positive and a negative integer.

    c. The product of an integer and zero.

33. Use your work from Questions 31 and 32 to solve the following problems.

    a. $2(-5) =$

    b. $5(2) =$

    c. $0 - 2(-5) =$

    d. $5(0) =$

    e. $4(2) + 1(-5) =$

    f. $2(3) - 3(-5) =$

Integer Games

Title of Model Instructional Unit: Integer Games

Embedded Assessment Question # _____ Page # _____

How could you improve your response to this question?

What part of this Model Instructional Unit is an example of your best work? Explain why you feel this is your best work.

What mathematical skills, strategies, or knowledge that you had prior to starting this Model Instructional Unit helped you to complete this activity?

What new mathematical skills, strategies, or knowledge did you obtain while completing this Model Instructional Unit?

Middle School Mathematics I

When Were You Born?

Contents

When Were You Born?

Part I

Claire read somewhere that more people are born in August than in any other month. Have your class form a single line in order of their birth months to see if what Claire read is true.

1. Record the birth-month data for your class using the three methods given below.

   a. **Method 1:** Count the number of students in your class born each month and record the data in the table below.

Class Member Birthday Months

Month	Number of Members
January	
February	
March	
April	
May	
June	
July	
August	
September	
October	
November	
December	

b. Method 2: Line up again by birth month. Now form a circle, standing shoulder-to-shoulder. Follow your teacher's directions for marking the circle and label the sections or sectors of the circle for each birth month on the ground or floor. You have represented the birth-month data in a **circle graph** or **pie graph**. Give your graph a title, label each sector with the appropriate month, and then sketch the graph onto the circle below.

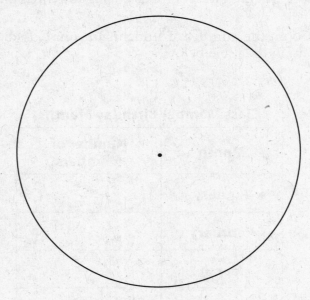

c. Method 3: Now line up in columns by birth month, the first column of people being those born in January, the second column being those born in February, and so on, in order to create a bar graph to represent the data. Have someone mark rectangles around the columns of people and mark a horizontal and a vertical axis. Title the graph. Label the month represented by each rectangle along the horizontal axis. On the vertical axis, mark off an appropriate scale. Then copy the bar graph in the space below.

2. Answer the following questions.

   a. What are the three methods you used to represent the birth-month data?

   Method 1:

   Method 2:

   Method 3:

   b. For each of the three methods, how would you determine the month(s) in which the most number of people were born?

   Method 1:

   Method 2:

   Method 3:

   c. Suppose you were given birth-month data from another class in the form of a table. Do you think it would be easier to more accurately draw a bar graph or a circle graph for the new data? Why?

Part II

Now look at some other birthday data.

IGLOO

Ice Cream Shop

3. The *Igloo Ice Cream Shop* has a birthday club. Each month they send a card with a coupon for a free ice cream treat to members born in that month. The following table shows the number of members with birthdays each month. Complete the table by finding the fraction of members and the percent of members born each month.

Igloo Ice Cream Shop Birthday Club

Month	Number of Members	Fraction of Members	Percent of Members
January	20		
February	22		
March	30		
April	18		
May	60		
June	30		
July	24		
August	36		
September	25		
October	40		
November	10		
December	45		

4. Complete the following.

    a. Draw a bar graph to represent the *Igloo Ice Cream Shop* birth-month data. Be sure to title your graph, label each axis, and show a scale on the vertical axis.

    b. Write two statements about the graph you just drew.

When Were You Born?

5. Use a protractor and the circles labeled Circle A, Circle B, Circle C, and Circle D (see end of this Unit) to answer the following questions:

   a. What is the sum of the measure of the four right angles in Circle A?

   b. What is the sum of the measures of the eight acute angles in Circle B?

   c. What is the sum of the measure of the four right angles in Circle C?

   d. What is the sum of the measures of the six acute angles in Circle D?

   e. Does size of a circle or the number of angles in a circle seem to affect the sum of the measures of the angles of a circle? Explain below.

   f. Based on your answers above, how many degrees are there in any circle?

6. a. What was the total number of members in the *Igloo Ice Cream Shop* birthday club?

   b. How does the total number of members of the *Igloo Ice Cream Shop* birthday club compare to the number of degrees in a circle?

7. Suppose that the members of the *Igloo Ice Cream Shop* birthday club lined up by birth month and formed a circle as your class did.

   a. How many degrees of the circle would be needed to represent the number of people in the *Igloo Ice Cream Shop* birthday club born in January?

   b. How many degrees of the circle would be needed to represent the number of people in the *Igloo Ice Cream Shop* birthday club born in October?

   c. How many people would each degree of the circle represent?

When Were You Born?

8. Complete the first two blank columns of the table by copying the information from the table in Question 3. Then complete the rest of the table to show what percent of 360° would be used in each sector of the circle graph and the number of degrees for each sector.

Igloo Ice Cream Shop Birthday Club

Month	Number of Members	Fraction of Members	Percent of Members	Percent of 360°	Number of Degrees
January	20				
February	22				
March	30				
April	18				
May	60				
June	30				
July	24				
August	36				
September	25				
October	40				
November	10				
December	45				

9. Use the circle at the end of this Unit to make a circle graph for the birth-month data shown in Question 8. Be sure to title the circle graph and label each sector with the correct month and percent.

10. Which two pairs of columns in the above table have the same values in them?

11. In a previous year the *Igloo Ice Cream Shop* birthday club had only 180 members. Complete the part of the table shown below for that year.

Igloo Ice Cream Shop Birthday Club in 2001

Month	Number of Members	Fraction of Members	Percent of Members	Percent of 360°	Number of Degrees
January	8				
February	10				
March	18				
April	12				

12. Are both pairs of columns that were equal in Question 8 still equal in Question 11? Explain below.

When Were You Born?

13. Suppose that for this year, the *Igloo Ice Cream Shop* has budgeted $800 for the birthday club expenses and they want to spend the same amount of money on each member. Make a recommendation to the manager as to how much of the budgeted amount of money should be spent each month. Be sure to explain to the manager how you arrived at your decision.

Igloo Ice Cream Shop
Monthly Birthday Club Budget

Month	Amount
January	
February	
March	
April	
May	
June	
July	
August	
September	
October	
November	
December	

Explanation:

When Were You Born?

Part III

14. Now look back at the birthday data from your class.

    a. What is the total number of people in your class birth-month data?

    b. For the data from your class, would it be useful to let one degree represent one person in making a circle graph? Explain below.

15. Copy the Number of Members from your table on the first page and then complete the rest of the table below.

Class Member Birth Months

Month	Number of Members	Fraction of Members	Percent of Members	Percent of 360° in a Circle Graph	Number of Degrees in a Circle Graph
January					
February					
March					
April					
May					
June					
July					
August					
September					
October					
November					
December					

16. Use the circle on the last page of this Unit to draw a circle graph for your class birth-month data. Be sure to title and label your graph. Then look to see if this graph appears similar to the one you drew in Part I.

17. a. About how many people are there in your entire school?

b. Assume that the percentages of birthdays each month is about the same for the entire school as they are for your class. Under this assumption, how many people in your school would have been born in January? In June?

c. Your principal would like to send out birthday cards at the beginning of each month to each of the students in your school who has a birthday in that particular month. She has put you in charge of deciding about how many cards she should order each month. In the space below, write a letter telling her how many cards you would suggest she order for each month. Be sure to explain how you decided. Also, tell her whether you think that using your class percents makes valid predictions for the entire school.

Circle A

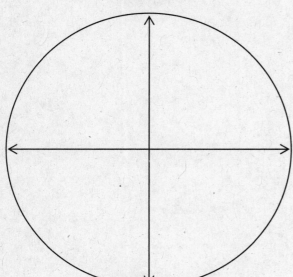

Circle B

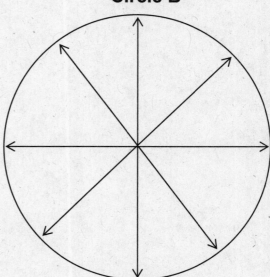

Circle C

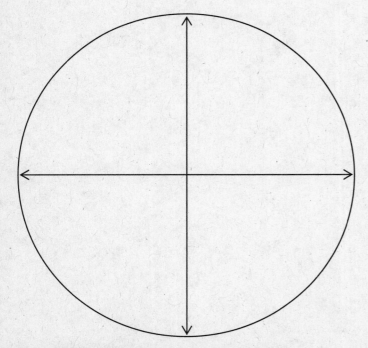

Circle D

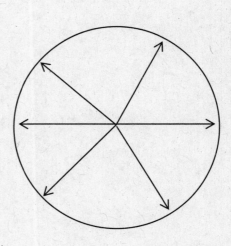

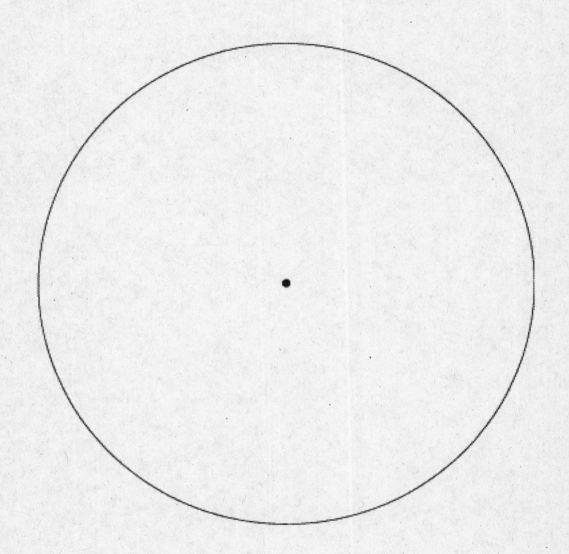

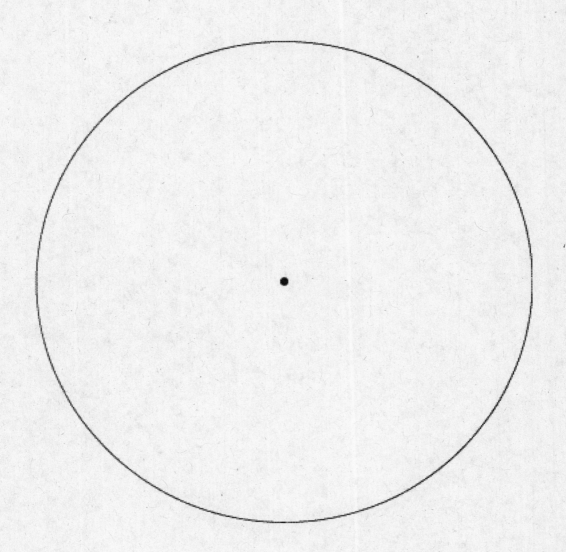

When Were You Born?

Title of Model Instructional Unit: When Were You Born?

Embedded Assessment Question # _____ Page # _____

How could you improve your response to this question?

What part of this Model Instructional Unit is an example of your best work? Explain why you feel this is your best work.

What mathematical skills, strategies, or knowledge that you had prior to starting this Model Instructional Unit helped you to complete this activity?

What new mathematical skills, strategies, or knowledge did you obtain while completing this Model Instructional Unit?

Middle School Mathematics I

Taking a Class Picture

Contents

Taking a Class Picture

STUDENT ACTIVITY

Introduction

Your mathematics teacher has given the class a new math project. The project is to describe your classmates using the results of a survey. It is easy for you to describe individual students in your classes, but you might have difficulty describing your classmates as a whole. Kai is a new student in your mathematics class. He often talks with you about his old school and seems to know all kinds of facts about the students in his former classes. Kai tells you that at his old school he was given a similar math project. You hope that this survey and your class project will help you to obtain a better picture of your classmates.

Part I

1. Try to read the message on the grid below.

2. Complete the following actions on the grid above.

   a. Redraw all vertical lines by moving them down three spaces.

   b. Redraw all horizontal lines by moving them up four spaces.

3. Read the message on the grid and write it in the space below.

4. All of the pieces of the letters used to write the message were given in the original grid. No pieces were added or deleted. Why was it so difficult to read the message at first?

Part II

In Part I, all of the pieces of a statement were given, yet it was impossible to read. In order to obtain a clear picture of what the pieces meant, it was necessary to rearrange the pieces in such a manner as to result in a meaningful conclusion.

The students in your class have completed a survey. The data collected in your survey are similar to the pieces in the statement. Although you have all of the pieces, it is difficult to draw meaningful conclusions from this data in their present form.

Collecting the data is only the first half of the project. The second half of this project is to summarize the findings to make conclusions about your class. Statisticians use various types of graphical displays to arrange data so that conclusions can be easily and quickly determined.

To help you understand this process, your teacher asks Kai to share the data he collected at his old school. The following list shows the genders of the students in Kai's former math class.

boy   boy   girl   boy   girl   boy   boy   girl   boy

boy   boy   girl   girl   girl   boy   girl   girl   girl

The only conclusion that you can reach immediately is that there were both boys and girls in the class. This of course, is something that you probably could have guessed.

A graphical display that is useful for summarizing data is a **pie chart**.

5. The pie chart for Kai's data is shown below. What does the pie chart *immediately* tell you about the students in Kai's former math class?

Kai's Math Class

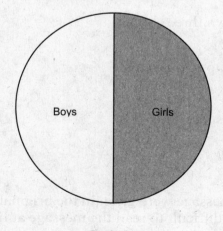

Gender

6. The pie chart below represents the students in Kai's former English class.

Kai's English Class

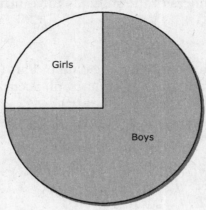

Gender

a. What does this pie chart tell you about the students in Kai's former English class?

b. Can the number of boys in this class be determined from the pie chart? Explain your reasoning.

c. There were 20 students in Kai's former English class. How many of the students were girls? Show how you arrived at your answer.

7. Use your class survey to complete the following.

    a. Make a list of the genders of the students in your math class.

    b. Create a pie chart that represents the data in Part (a). The broken lines are provided to assist you in making your graph accurate. Be certain to label your graph.

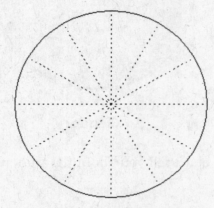

8. Use your class survey to complete the following.

    a. Make a list of the eye colors of the students in your math class.

    b. Once again, the picture of the data is not immediately clear from the list. Create a pie chart that represents the data in Part (a). The broken lines are provided to assist you in making your graph accurate. Be certain to label your graph.

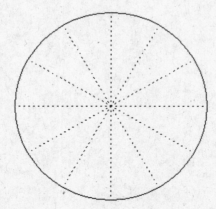

Taking a Class Picture

Pie charts help us to quickly examine a data set. Another commonly used graphical display is a **bar chart**. Each bar of a bar chart represents a different category. The height of the bar charts can be labeled with the **count** for each category or the **percent** for each category. The following bar charts represent the genders of the students in Kai's former math class.

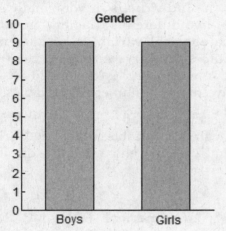
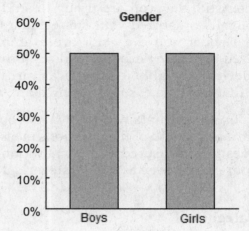

9. Which bar chart above gives you more information than the pie chart in Question 5? Explain your reasoning.

10. Create a bar chart below for the genders of the students in your math class. Mark the vertical axis with percents.

11. Create a bar chart below for the eye colors of the students in your math class. Mark the vertical axis with counts.

Taking a Class Picture

STUDENT ACTIVITY (continued)

Part III

Your class survey contains 16 questions. Each question represents a **variable**, or characteristic, that you are trying to study about the **individuals** in your math class. You have already organized your survey data based on two different variables – gender and eye color. Gender and eye color are examples of **categorical variables** because the data is organized by placing each individual in the class into a category. Another type of variable is a **numerical variable**. Numerical variables occur when data is organized by numerical values that can be measured. Weight and age are examples of numerical variables.

12. Your survey contained 16 different questions, each designed to measure a different variable. Some of the questions measured categorical variables and some of the questions measured numerical variables. Identify each of the remaining questions in your class survey as being categorical or numerical.

Categorical   **Numerical**

#2. Gender

#6. Eye Color

SpringBoard™ Mathematics with Meaning
©2005 College Entrance Examination Board

Middle School Mathematics I • Taking a Class Picture
Student Version 2.0

128

When a variable is represented by a number, it does not automatically make the variable numerical. Numerical variables have values for which numerical calculations, such as averages or addition, would make sense. If either of those operations do not make sense, the variable is categorical.

For example, your survey might have asked your classmates to list the room number of their favorite teacher. Although we can compute an average room number for the favorite teacher, it does not have any real-world meaning. Room numbers are categorical variables.

13. Go back through your list of numerical variables in Question 12 and determine whether any of the numerical variables should be moved to your list of categorical variables.

14. At the end of the class survey, you were asked to write a question to be included in the survey.

    a. Write your question below and indicate whether it measures a categorical variable or a numerical variable.

    b. If your question measured a numerical variable, write a question below that measures a categorical variable. If your question measured a categorical variable, write a question below that measures a numerical variable.

Taking a Class Picture

Part IV

Categorical variables are best displayed by pie charts and bar graphs. The goal in displaying the data is to be able to make observations and quickly understand the data set. For numerical variables, the goal is the same, but pie charts and bar graphs are not the appropriate types of graphical displays for numerical variables. When the data is numerical, **dot plots** and **stem plots** are two commonly used graphical displays.

The following is a list of the shoe sizes of the students in Kai's former math class.

$$2\tfrac{1}{2} \quad 4 \quad 5\tfrac{1}{2} \quad 2 \quad 6\tfrac{1}{2} \quad 5\tfrac{1}{2} \quad 5 \quad 1 \quad 4\tfrac{1}{2}$$

$$3\tfrac{1}{2} \quad 2\tfrac{1}{2} \quad 8 \quad 5 \quad 4 \quad 3\tfrac{1}{2} \quad 7 \quad 2\tfrac{1}{2} \quad 6\tfrac{1}{2}$$

The teacher showed the class how to use the above data to create the following **dot plot**.

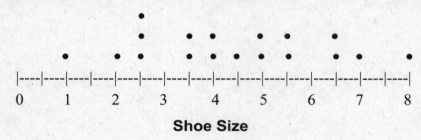

Shoe Size

15. Answer the following questions regarding the shoe sizes of the students in Kai's former math class. Indicate whether you used the *list* of the shoe sizes or the *dot plot* to answer each question.

    a. How many students wear a size 4 shoe?

    b. What is the most common shoe size?

    c. How many students wear a shoe that is smaller than size 6?

    d. What is the largest shoe size of all the students in the class?

    e. Estimate the typical shoe size for students in this class.

    f. What is the range of shoe sizes for students in this class?

16. All of the answers in Question 15 could have been determined using only Kai's list of shoe sizes. Explain why it was better to use the dot plot.

17. Use your class survey to complete the following.

  a. Make a list of the shoe sizes of the students in your math class.

  b. Use the shoe size data in Part (a) to create a dot plot in the space below. Be certain to label your graph.

  c. Give a brief summary of what the dot plot in Part (b) tells you about the shoe sizes of the students in your math class.

18. Create a dot plot for the "Total number of letters in your full name" data from your class survey and give a brief summary of what the dot plot tells you about the students in your math class.

19. The results from Kai's former math class for the question, "Minutes that it took you to get ready for school today" data are shown below.

48	90	35	10	45	10	20	53	20
30	30	10	52	12	60	25	5	45

Explain why it would be difficult to create a dot plot for the data above.

The teacher uses the data for the "Minutes that it took you to get ready for school today" from Kai's former math class to create the following **stem plot**. The legend in the stem plot tells that the number 90 is shown as 9 | 0 where 9 is the stem. In the stem plot, 5 | 2 3 represents both 52 and 53.

```
0 | 5              Minutes that it took you to
1 | 0 0 0 2        get ready for school today
2 | 0 0 5
3 | 0 0 5
4 | 5 5 8
5 | 2 3
6 | 0
7 |
8 |
9 | 0              Legend:  9 | 0 = 90
```

20. Answer the following questions regarding the time it took the students in Kai's former math class to get ready for school. Indicate whether you used the *list* of the data or the *stem plot* to answer each question.

   a. How many students took 30 minutes to get ready for school?

   b. What is the most common amount time that it took students to get ready for school?

   c. How many students took *more* than 30 minutes to get ready for school?

   d. Estimate the typical amount of time that it took for a student to get ready for school.

   e. What is the range of the amount of time that it took for students to get ready for school?

   f. Is there a student that does not fit in the pattern of the rest of the class? Explain your reasoning.

Part V

Remember that the reason for using a graphical display was to quickly observe and understand the data. For categorical data we summarize by giving the proportions or counts of the data that fall into each of the categories. For numerical data, we will use a different summary method. In the summary of numerical data we will determine the **center** of the data, the **spread** of the data, and we will look for **outliers**.

21. List the part(s) of Question 20 (by letter) that determine the following.

    a. The center of Kai's data.

    b. The spread of Kai's data.

    c. The outliers in Kai's data.

In order to determine the center or typical value of a data set, there are three commonly used measures. These three measures are the **mean**, the **median**, and the **mode**.

To find the *mean*, add all of the data values and then divide by the total number of data items.

22. Determine the mean of the "Minutes that it took you to get ready for school today" data for Kai's former math class.

To find the *median*, arrange all of the data items in order from smallest to largest. The *median* is the number that is exactly in the middle position of the list.

- If the list has an odd number of data items, the median is a member of the list.
- If the list has an even number of data items, the median is the mean of the middle two data items.

23. After examining the following lists and their medians, determine the median of the "Minutes that it took you to get ready for school today" data for Kai's former math class.

6 10 13 17 20
⇑
median = 13

6 10 13 13 20
⇑
median = 13

6 10 13 13 17 20
⇑
median = 13

6 10 13 18 20 24
⇑
median = 15.5

To find the *mode*, look for the data item that occurs most often.

24. Determine the mode of the "Minutes that it took you to get ready for school today" data for Kai's former math class.

The spread of the data is the next piece in the summary for a numerical variable. There are many different measures of how data is spread out, but the easiest measure of spread is the **range**. The *range* is equal to the highest data value minus the lowest data value.

25. Find the mean, median, and range of the following data sets.

    a. 6   8   10

    b. 8   8   8

    c. 2   8   14

26. The centers of the three data sets would lead you to believe that the three data sets are identical. What do the ranges of the data sets tell you that the measures of center do not?

The final piece in a summary for a numerical variable is to determine if there are any **outliers**. *Outliers* are individual data points that do not fit the overall pattern of the data set. Not all data sets will contain outliers.

27. Using the "Minutes that it took you to get ready for school today" data for Kai's former math class, determine the range and identify any outliers.

28. Create a stem plot for the "Time that it took you to get ready for school today" data from the students in your math class.

29. Write a brief description for the "Time that it took you to get ready for school today" data from the students in your math class. Use median as your measure of center, range as your measure of spread, and identify any outliers in the data set.

30. In Question 18, you were asked to create a dot plot for the "Total number of letters in your full name" data from your class survey and write a brief summary about the students in your class based on your dot plot. Rewrite your summary, making sure to include all three parts of a summary for a numerical variable. Use median as your measure of center.

31. You have used four different graphical displays to help you obtain a better picture of the students in your math class. Complete the following table concerning these graphical displays.

Type of Graphical Display	Type of Variable Measured	Summary Information
1.		
2.		
3.		
4.		

TAKING A CLASS PICTURE SURVEY

Please answer the following questions about yourself to the best of your ability. This is an anonymous survey: **do not** put your name on this survey.

1. Total number of letters in your full name
    (include first, middle, and last names)   _____

2. Gender (boy or girl)   _____

3. Number of the month in which you were born
    (January = 1, February = 2, etc.)   _____

4. Height (rounded off, in inches)   _____

5. Shoe size   _____

6. Eye color   _____

7. Left- or right-handed   _____

8. Number of brothers and sisters that you have   _____

9. Number of hours of sleep that you had last night   _____

10. Minutes that it took you to get ready for school today   _____

11. Minutes that it took you to travel to school today   _____

12. Where do you sit in this classroom? (front, middle, or back) _____

13. Favorite school subject   _____

14. Total number of movies that you viewed last week
    (movie theater + rentals + TV)   _____

15. Favorite fast food restaurant   _____

16. Total ounces of soda consumed yesterday
    (1 can = 12 oz., 1 bottle = 16 oz.)   _____

Suppose that you were conducting a survey to find out more information about your classmates. Write a question below that you would include in your survey.

Taking a Class Picture

Title of Model Instructional Unit: Taking a Class Picture

Embedded Assessment Question # _____ Page # _____

How could you improve your response to this question?

What part of this Model Instructional Unit is an example of your best work? Explain why you feel this is your best work.

What mathematical skills, strategies, or knowledge that you had prior to starting this Model Instructional Unit helped you to complete this activity?

What new mathematical skills, strategies, or knowledge did you obtain while completing this Model Instructional Unit?

Middle School Mathematics I

In a Whirl

Contents

In a Whirl

Part I

Amalia found several faces for spinners belonging to some old spinner games but could not find the rules for any of the games. Some of the old spinner faces are shown below.

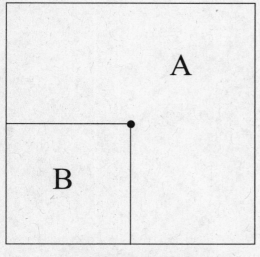

Spinner Face 1

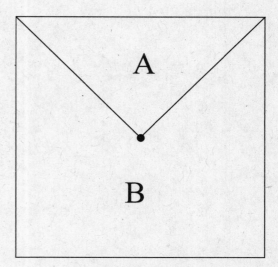

Spinner Face 2

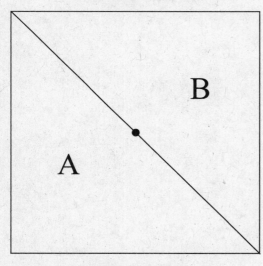

Spinner Face 3

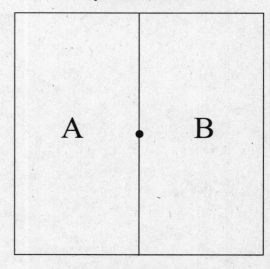

Spinner Face 4

In a Whirl

Each of the spinner faces is a square that is separated into two parts, labeled A and B. The dot on each spinner face locates where the spinner would be attached. Unfortunately, the spinners are not attached to these spinner faces. But Amalia knows that she can still use these spinner faces by attaching a paper clip and a pencil. Here's how it works.

> Place the paper clip so that the center of the spinner face is inside one of its loops; then place the pencil so that its point rests on the center dot of the spinner face. When the paper clip is "flicked" with a finger, it will spin around the pencil point until it stops. The center of the outer loop of the paper clip will point to a lettered section of the spinner. If the paper clip points to a line, the spin will not count; instead, another spin will be necessary.

Amalia remembers that these spinner faces were used for a two-player game. She recalls that players choose one letter that will be their letter for all spins. She also remembers that players then score points whenever the spinner lands on their letter. Each player spins five times. The player with the greatest number of points at the end of the game wins the game.

1. Use a paper clip and a pencil to practice flicking the paper clip. Then answer the following questions.

   a. Which letter would you choose as your letter in Amalia's two-player game with Spinner Face 1? Explain why you selected the letter you chose.

   b. Which letter would you choose as your letter in Amalia's two-player game with Spinner Face 2? Explain why you selected the letter you chose.

   c. Which letter would you choose as your letter in Amalia's two-player game with Spinner Face 3? Explain why you selected the letter you chose.

   d. Which letter would you choose as your letter in Amalia's two-player game with Spinner Face 4? Explain why you selected the letter you chose.

2. Try five spins on each spinner face. Before each spin, write down the letter that you think will be the outcome of the spin. Use the tables below to record your letter choice before each spin, the letter outcome after the spin, and the number of times you were correct about the outcome.

		Spin 1	Spin 2	Spin 3	Spin 4	Spin 5	Number of Correct Guesses
Face 1	Letter Guess Before Spin						
	Letter Outcome After Spin						

		Spin 1	Spin 2	Spin 3	Spin 4	Spin 5	Number of Correct Guesses
Face 2	Letter Guess Before Spin						
	Letter Outcome After Spin						

		Spin 1	Spin 2	Spin 3	Spin 4	Spin 5	Number of Correct Guesses
Face 3	Letter Guess Before Spin						
	Letter Outcome After Spin						

		Spin 1	Spin 2	Spin 3	Spin 4	Spin 5	Number of Correct Guesses
Face 4	Letter Guess Before Spin						
	Letter Outcome After Spin						

3. Work with a classmate to compare results recorded in Question 2 and to answer the following.

   a. For which spinner face(s) were you or your partner able to make the highest number of correct guesses?

   b. Did the spinner face layout of your answer in Part (a) help you in any way to make a high number of correct guesses? Explain below.

   c. For which spinner face(s) did you or your partner make the lowest number of correct guesses?

   d. Did the spinner face layout in your answer in Part (c) hurt you in any way to make a low number of correct guesses? Explain below.

   e. Is it possible to select the correct outcome of every spin on Face 1? Explain why or why not.

   f. Is it possible to select the correct outcome of every spin on Face 3? Explain why or why not.

4. A definition for the word **random** is **unpredictable**.

   a. Are the outcomes of spins on Spinner Faces 1 and 2 random? Explain below.

   b. Are the outcomes of spins on Spinner Faces 3 and 4 random? Explain below.

In a Whirl

5. Consider the likelihood of the outcomes on each of the spinner faces.

    a. Rate the outcomes as least likely, most likely, or equally likely.

Spinner Face 1

Outcome A: Outcome B:

Rating is_____   Rating is_____

Spinner Face 2

Outcome A: Outcome B:

Rating is_____   Rating is_____

Spinner Face 3

Outcome A: Outcome B:

Rating is_____   Rating is_____

Spinner Face 4

Outcome A: Outcome B:

Rating is_____   Rating is_____

    b. Explain the reasoning used to make your ratings of likelihood for the outcomes on each of the spinner faces.

c. A student named Frank is puzzled because when he flicked the spinner using Spinner Face 1, his outcome was *not* the most likely outcome. Frank asks, "Shouldn't I have gotten the most likely outcome?" Give Frank an explanation about what most likely outcome really means so that he will no longer be puzzled.

6. Laura and Hardy are two students whose answers to the ratings of likelihood in Question 5(a) were exactly the same. But the reasoning that Laura and Hardy used to determine their ratings was different. Here is the reasoning each student gave.

Laura's reasoning: "I used the angle opening around the center of the square to determine the likelihood of each outcome. Larger angle openings for a letter mean a larger likelihood for the letter outcome."

Hardy's reasoning: "I used the area of the region labeled by the letter to determine the likelihood of each outcome. Larger areas for a letter mean a larger likelihood for the letter outcome."

Which student's reasoning is correct? Explain why.

Part II Introducing Probability as a Measure of Likelihood

Probability in mathematics is the measure of the likelihood of a random outcome. In Part I, you learned that even though outcomes were random or unpredictable, outcomes for the spinner faces were least likely, most likely, or equally likely to occur. To **measure the likelihood** means to attach a number to an outcome that tells someone just how likely that outcome is to occur.

7. Use Spinner Faces 1 and 3 for this investigation.

    a. Estimate the number of times each outcome listed in the table below would occur for 100 spins or trials on the indicated spinner face.

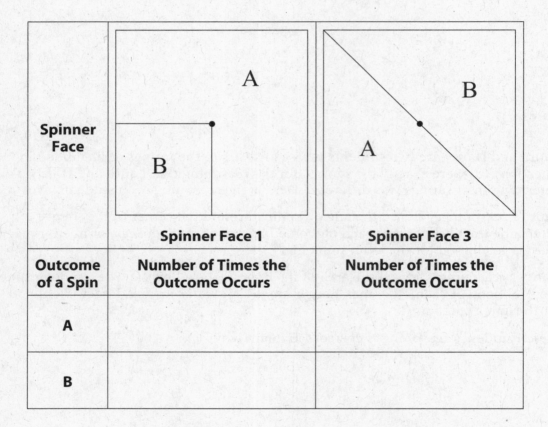

Spinner Face	Spinner Face 1	Spinner Face 3
Outcome of a Spin	**Number of Times the Outcome Occurs**	**Number of Times the Outcome Occurs**
A		
B		

    b. Write an explanation for the reasoning used to arrive at your estimates.

In a Whirl

Probability uses a ratio to measure the likelihood of a random outcome. If an experiment has two equally likely outcomes, then the probability of each of the outcomes is $\frac{1}{2}$. If an experiment has three equally likely outcomes, then the probability of each of the outcomes is $\frac{1}{3}$, and so on.

8. Spinner Face 3 is again shown below.

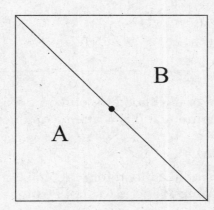

a. Are the outcomes of Spinner Face 3 equally likely outcomes? Explain below.

b. Express the measure of likelihood for outcome A as a ratio. This ratio is called the **probability of outcome A** and is written P(spinner points to A).

   P(spinner points to A) =

c. Express the measure of likelihood for outcome B as a ratio. This ratio is called the **probability of outcome B** and is written P(spinner points to B).

   P(spinner points to B) =

d. Multiply your ratios from Parts (b) and (c) by 100 spins. Compare your answers to your estimates for outcomes A and B in the table in Question 7. Explain why they should agree.

9. Spinner Face 1 is again shown below.

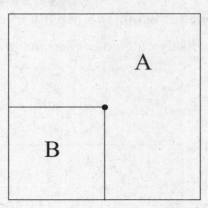

a. Express the measure of likelihood for outcome A as a ratio. This ratio is called the **probability of outcome A** and is written P(spinner points to A).

P(spinner points to A) =

b. Express the measure of likelihood for outcome B as a ratio. This ratio is called the **probability of outcome B** and is written P(spinner points to B).

P(spinner points to B) =

10. Use the blank square spinner faces given below to draw spinner faces that have properties described in Parts (a) and (b), as follows.

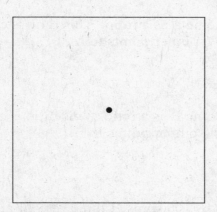

Spinner Face for Part (a)

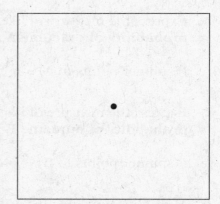

Spinner Face for Part (b)

a. A spinner face with four sections labeled A, B, C, and D and these four sections are equally likely outcomes on the spinner.

b. A spinner face with three sections labeled A, B, and C and these three sections are outcomes on the spinner with the following probabilities:

P(spinner points to A) = $\dfrac{1}{4}$ P(spinner points to B) = $\dfrac{1}{2}$

P(spinner points to C) = $\dfrac{1}{4}$

c. Explain the reasoning you used to construct the spinner faces in Parts (a) and (b).

Part III   Experimenting with Probability

Probability provides us with a mathematical tool to predict an estimate for the number of times an outcome of an experiment will occur when a given number of trials are carried out. We will test the ability of probability as a theoretical prediction tool by investigating two experiments.

Spinner Face 1 Experiment	**Spinner Face 2 Experiment**
The trial in this experiment will be to spin a paper clip on the spinner face.	The trial in this experiment will be to spin a paper clip on the spinner face.
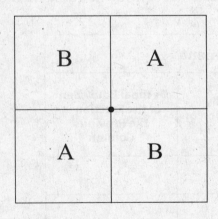	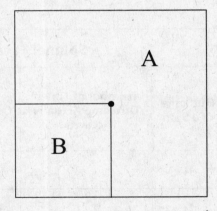
This experiment will consist of 24 trials.	This experiment will consist of 24 trials.

11. You and your partner should select one of the spinner experiments described.

    a. The first step is to find the theoretical probability of each outcome. Next, determine the theoretical probability as a decimal number and place it appropriately in the table below. Write a brief description of how you arrived at the theoretical probability in the space below the table.

Spinner Face _____ Experiment		
Outcome of a Spin	Theoretical Probability of the Outcome as a Fraction	Theoretical Probability of the Outcome as a Decimal
A		
B		

    b. Carry out 24 trials and record the number of times each outcome occurs in the table below. Indicate "the number of times each outcome actually occurred as a fraction of the total number of trials" and the "decimal equivalent of the fraction."

Spinner Face _____ Experiment			
Outcome of a Spin	Number of Times Outcome Actually Occurred	Number of Times Outcome Actually Occurred as a Fraction of the Total Number of Trials	Decimal Equivalent of the Fraction in the Previous Column
A			
B			
Total	24	24	

c. Share your spinner experiment results with your partner. With your partner, make a common list of observations. For example, indicate any expectations confirmed or indicate any surprising outcomes.

d. Compare the decimal numbers in the last two columns of the tables in Parts (a) and (b). Do the decimal numbers from the 24 trials match the predicted theoretical decimal numbers? Should the decimal numbers be expected to match well? Explain below.

12. Collect data of the trials for each of the spinner experiments from other students in class who conducted these experiments.

a. Summarize the class data in the following two tables.

Class Results for Spinner Experiment 1				
Outcome of a Spin	Number of Times Outcome Actually Occurred	Number of Times Outcome Actually Occurred as a Fraction of the Total Number of Trials	Decimal Equivalent of the Fraction in the Previous Column	Theoretical Probability of the Outcome as a Decimal
A				
B				
Total				

Class Results for Spinner Experiment 2				
Outcome of a Spin	Number of Times Outcome Actually Occurred	Number of Times Outcome Actually Occurred as a Fraction of the Total Number of Trials	Decimal Equivalent of the Fraction in the Previous Column	Theoretical Probability of the Outcome as a Decimal
A				
B				
Total				

b. Compare the decimal numbers in the last two columns of the tables in Part (a). For the spinner face experiment you conducted, do the decimal numbers from the total class trials match, better or worse, with the predicted theoretical decimal numbers than those two decimal numbers in your individual data? Should the decimal numbers be expected to match better or worse? Explain below.

Part IV

Amalia found another square spinner face. This new square spinner face is shown below.

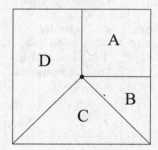

13. List all of the outcomes of a trial spin using the new square spinner face.

14. Use the notation P(spinner points to A) to denote the probability of outcome A from a trial spin. This notation is called **probability notation**.

    a. Find P(spinner points to A).

    b. Find P(spinner points to B).

    c. Find P(spinner points to C).

    d. Find P(spinner points to D).

    e. Are the outcomes of the ABCD spinner equally likely outcomes? Write a brief explanation to support your answer.

15. Amalia does not have the rules that go with the ABCD spinner face. But she does remember that this game is a two-player game in which each player has two letters. Each player spins the spinner six times. A player scores a point whenever the spinner lands on his or her letter. The player with the greatest score at the end of the game wins the game.

   a. Which two letters would you choose and why?

   b. Amalia remembers that the game is fair to each player. What letters should each player get to make this a fair game? Explain the reasoning used to support your answer.

Part V

Another spinner in Amalia's collection of spinner faces is the following GHI spinner face.

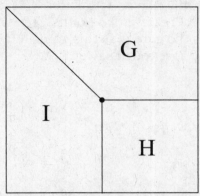

16. Find the following probabilities for the above spinner face.

    a. P(spinner points to G) =

    b. P(spinner points to H) =

    c. P(spinner points to I) =

17. Suppose the GHI spinner face given above is used for a three-player game with the following rules. Each player chooses a different letter and spins the spinner 16 times. A player scores a point whenever the spinner lands on his or her letter. The player with the greatest score at the end of the game wins the game. Is this game a fair game to all the players? Write a brief explanation to support your answer.

18. Suppose the GHI spinner face shown on the previous page is used for a three-player game with the following rules. Each player chooses a different letter and spins the spinner 16 times. But instead of a player receiving one point whenever the spinner lands on his or her letter, the player with letter H receives three points while the players with letters G and I receive two points. The player with the greatest score at the end of the game wins the game. Is this game a fair game to all the players? Write a brief explanation to support your answer.

In a Whirl

Title of Model Instructional Unit: In a Whirl

Embedded Assessment Question # _____ Page # _____

How could you improve your response to this question?

What part of this Model Instructional Unit is an example of your best work? Explain why you feel this is your best work.

What mathematical skills, strategies, or knowledge that you had prior to starting this Model Instructional Unit helped you to complete this activity?

What new mathematical skills, strategies, or knowledge did you obtain while completing this Model Instructional Unit?

Middle School Mathematics I

Penny Stacking

Contents

Introduction

What is the height of a stack of 150 pennies? Make your best guess and write it in the space below. Be sure to include units.

A stack of 150 pennies is _____ tall.

What reasons did you have for making your prediction? Clearly explain your thinking.

Penny Stacking

Initial Exploration

1. Using the ruler and pennies that are provided, measure and record the heights of the stacks of pennies listed in the table below.

Number of Pennies	25	10	15	20
Height of Stack (in mm)				

2. Write a ratio that relates the number of pennies to the height in a stack that has:

   a. 15 pennies _____

   b. 25 pennies _____

   c. 20 pennies _____

   d. 10 pennies _____

3. What is true about the ratios in Question 2? Explain below.

4. Write a ratio that relates the height of the stack to the number of pennies in the stack for stacks with:

   a. 15 pennies _____

   b. 25 pennies _____

   c. 20 pennies _____

   d. 10 pennies _____

5. What is true about the ratios in Question 4? Explain below.

Part I

6. Write an equation that uses two of the ratios in Question 2.

7. Write an equation that uses two of the ratios in Question 4.

8. What is each of these equations called?

Part II

9. Suppose you are asked to find the height of a stack of 60 pennies. What would you do to find the height of that stack? Explain below.

10. Suppose you were asked to find the height of a stack of 372 pennies. What would you do to find the height of that stack? Explain below.

11. Are your methods for answering Questions 9 and 10 different? If so, explain.

12. Suppose you are asked to find how many pennies are in a stack that is 70 mm high. What would you do to find the number of pennies in the stack? Explain below.

13. Suppose you are asked to find how many pennies are in a stack 1 meter high. What would you do to find the number of pennies in the stack? Explain below.

14. Are your methods for answering Questions 12 and 13 different? If so, explain.

Part III

15. Graph the data from Question 1 on the graph below.

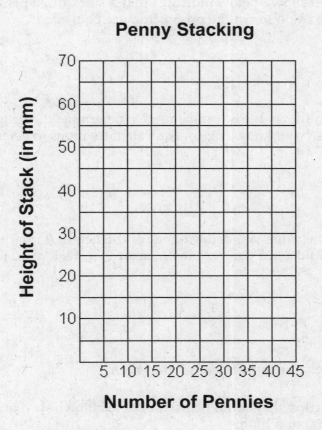

Penny Stacking

Height of Stack (in mm)

Number of Pennies

16. Use the graph to predict the height of a stack of 35 pennies. Explain below.

17. Use the graph to predict the number of pennies in a stack that is 60 mm high. Explain below.

18. How accurate are your predictions in Questions 16 and 17? Why?

Part IV

19. Assume that a stack of five pennies is 7 mm high.

    a. The proportion shown below indicates that a stack of 20 pennies is 28 mm high. Verify that the fractions in the proportion are equivalent.

$$\frac{7}{5} = \frac{28}{20}$$

    b. The proportion shown below can be used to determine the height h of a stack of 60 pennies. Use your knowledge of equivalent fractions to determine the value of h.

$$\frac{7}{5} = \frac{h}{60}$$

    c. Discuss why the value you determined for the height h might not be the same as the height you would get if you actually measured a stack of 60 pennies.

20. Assume that a stack of five pennies is 7 mm high.

    a. Write a proportion that could be used to determine how many pennies p are in a stack that is 100 mm high.

    b. Can you solve the proportion in Part (a) using your knowledge of equivalent fractions? Explain why or why not.

21. Use a proportion to make a better estimate than your original guess for the height of a stack of 150 pennies. Assume that a stack of five pennies is 7 mm high. Explain how you determined your answer.

22. How close was your original guess at the beginning of this Unit to your answer in Question 21?

Penny Stacking

Title of Model Instructional Unit: Penny Stacking

Embedded Assessment Question # _____   Page # _____

How could you improve your response to this question?

What part of this Model Instructional Unit is an example of your best work? Explain why you feel this is your best work.

What mathematical skills, strategies, or knowledge that you had prior to starting this Model Instructional Unit helped you to complete this activity?

What new mathematical skills, strategies, or knowledge did you obtain while completing this Model Instructional Unit?

Middle School Mathematics I

What's My Name?

Contents

What's My Name?

Introduction

Jonathan Paul Jones is a math teacher. His students call him Mr. Jones; the teachers at his school call him Jonathan; his close family calls him J.P.; and friends from high school and college call him Jon. Just as this one person has many names, there are often many ways to name geometric figures. In this activity you will explore ways to name geometric figures and then practice using the names correctly by playing a game.

Part I

The simplest geometric figure is called a **point**. To illustrate a point, we draw a dot. Points are named with capital letters, as shown below.

A •

B •   **C** •

1. What are the names of the three points drawn above?

2. Geometric figures are made up of points. Some geometric figures are pictured below. What is the name of each geometric figure?

    a. ←――――――――→

    b. •――――――――→

    c. •――――――――•

3. What geometric figure would best represent the following?

    a. A beam of light from a flashlight

    b. A city on a map

    c. A straight road between two cities

What's My Name?

When drawing lines, rays, and line segments, not all of the points that make up the figure are shown as dots. Some points are shown as dots to locate special positions or so that the points can be used to name the figure.

The following are examples of notation used to name lines, rays, and line segments.

Lines	Rays	Line Segments
$\overleftrightarrow{AB}$	$\overrightarrow{FH}$	$\overline{DE}$
$\overleftrightarrow{CA}$	$\overrightarrow{FG}$	$\overline{ED}$
$\overleftrightarrow{BA}$	ray FH	line segment DE
$\overleftrightarrow{AC}$	ray FG	line segment ED
line AB		
line AC		
ℓ		

4. Based on the examples for naming a line shown in the table above, describe what you think are considered acceptable ways to name a line.

5. Is $\overleftrightarrow{ABC}$ an acceptable name for a line? Explain your reasoning.

6. Use acceptable notation to give several names for the line shown below.

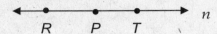

7. Based on the examples for naming a ray shown in the table on the previous page, describe what you think are considered acceptable ways to name a ray.

8. Is $\overrightarrow{NE}$ an acceptable name for the ray shown below? Explain your reasoning.

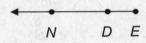

9. Based on the examples for naming a segment shown in the table on the previous page, describe what you think are considered acceptable ways to name a line segment.

10. Use acceptable notation to give two names for the line segment shown below.

Part II

An **angle** is formed by two rays that begin at the same point. The point is called the **vertex** and the rays are called the **sides of the angle**.

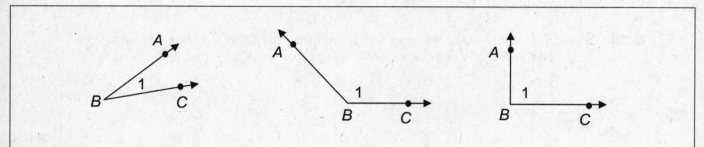

Correct Names for the Angles	Incorrect Names for the Angles
∠ABC	∠ACB
∠CBA	∠BAC
∠B	∠AB
∠1	∠BCA
	∠CB

11. Based on the examples for naming an angle shown in the table above, describe what you think are considered acceptable ways to name an angle.

12. In the figure below, is there a problem with naming an angle ∠B? Explain your reasoning.

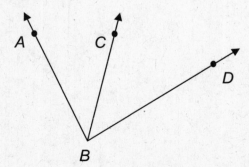

What's My Name?

The following are examples of different types of angles.

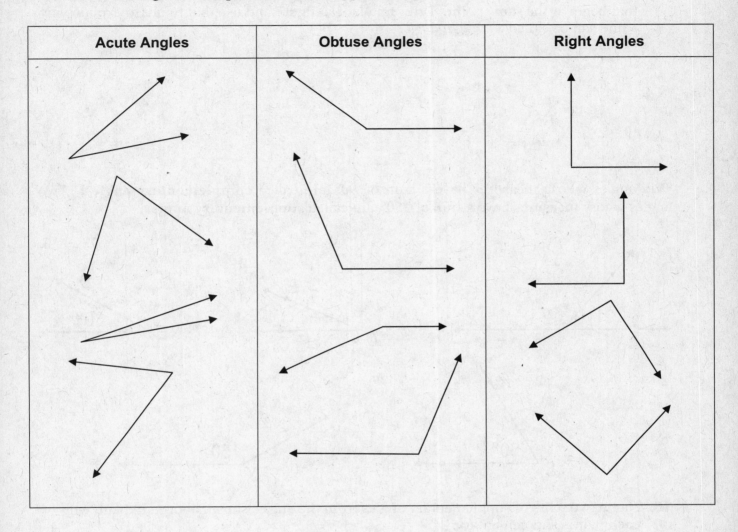

Acute Angles	Obtuse Angles	Right Angles

13. Based on the examples in the table above, write a definition for each type of angle.

    a. Acute angle

    b. Obtuse angle

    c. Right angle

14. A line is sometimes called a **straight angle**. Recall that an **angle** is formed by two rays that begin at the same point. Draw and label a figure and use that figure to explain why a line can be called a *straight angle*.

Two angles whose measures have a sum of 90° are called **complementary angles**. Two angles whose measures have a sum of 180° are called **supplementary angles**.

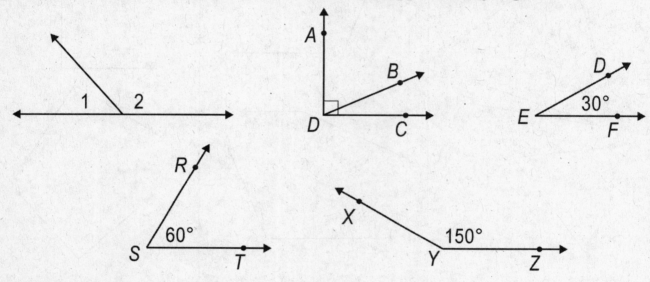

15. Name two pairs of supplementary angles from the angles shown above. Explain why each pair is supplementary.

16. Name two pairs of complementary angles from the angles shown on the previous page. Explain why each pair is complementary.

17. In the figures shown on the previous page, there are two pairs of angles known as **adjacent angles**. One pair is ∠1 and ∠2 and the other pair is ∠ADB and ∠BDC. Based on these examples, explain what is meant by *adjacent angles*.

18. Refer to the figure below to answer the following questions.

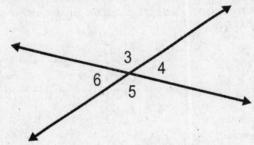

   a. Name two angles that are supplementary to ∠4.

   b. The angles you named in Part (a) are called **vertical angles**. Explain why these angles must have the same measure.

   c. Name another pair of vertical angles shown in the figure above.

What's My Name?

A **plane** is a flat surface that extends in all directions without ending. Lines that lie in a plane and do not cross or intersect are called **parallel lines**. Two lines that meet to form right angles are called **perpendicular lines**. If line *WX* and line *YZ* are *parallel*, we can use the notation $\overleftrightarrow{WX} \parallel \overleftrightarrow{YZ}$. If line *WX* and line *YZ* are *perpendicular*, we can use the notation $\overleftrightarrow{WX} \perp \overleftrightarrow{YZ}$.

19. Use the notation described above to name each pair of lines that appear to be perpendicular or parallel in the figure below.

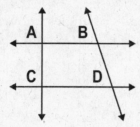

Part III

There are special names for some line segments associated with circles. Examples of these line segments are shown below.

Radius	Chord	Diameter

20. Based on the examples in the table on the previous page, write a definition for each of the following terms.

    a. Radius

    b. Chord

    c. Diameter

21. For the figure below, name all of the given types of line segments.

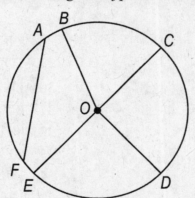

    a. Radii

    b. Diameters

    c. Chords

Part IV *What's My Name?* Game

The directions for setting up and playing the *What's My Name?* game follow.

1. Your game card has 24 empty boxes. Randomly fill in the empty boxes on the game card with 24 of the 36 statements listed below.

2. As your teacher reveals each of the game diagrams, look below for the correct notation used to name the geometric figure.

3. When you find an answer below, cross it out. If you do not find an answer, do nothing.

4. You win the game when five squares in a row have been crossed out.

1. $\overline{DB}$	19. $\overrightarrow{QP}$
2. $\overleftrightarrow{DB}$	20. radius of $\odot R$
3. $\overrightarrow{DB}$	21. diameter of $\odot R$
4. $\overrightarrow{BD}$	22. chord of $\odot R$
5. vertical angles	23. acute angle T
6. complementary angles	24. obtuse angle T
7. $\overrightarrow{BC}$	25. right angle T
8. $\overline{CB}$	26. $\overrightarrow{PQ}$
9. $\overrightarrow{CB}$	27. $\angle 2$
10. $\overrightarrow{BC}$	28. $\angle WZY$
11. $\overrightarrow{PQ}$	29. $\angle YWZ$
12. $\angle R$	30. $\overline{YW}$
13. supplementary angles	31. $\overrightarrow{WY}$
14. $\angle PQR$	32. $\overrightarrow{WZ}$
15. adjacent angles	33. $\overline{ZY}$
16. right angle ABC	34. $\overrightarrow{ZW}$
17. acute angle ABC	35. parallel lines
18. obtuse angle ABC	36. perpendicular lines

Game Card

What's My Name?

		Free Space		

What's My Name?

Title of Model Instructional Unit: What's My Name?

Embedded Assessment Question # _____ Page # _____

How could you improve your response to this question?

What part of this Model Instructional Unit is an example of your best work? Explain why you feel this is your best work.

What mathematical skills, strategies, or knowledge that you had prior to starting this Model Instructional Unit helped you to complete this activity?

What new mathematical skills, strategies, or knowledge did you obtain while completing this Model Instructional Unit?

Middle School Mathematics I

The Dot Game

Contents

The Dot Game

Have you ever played *The Dot Game*? Here is your chance to play the game *and* please your teacher! Even if you are familiar with the game, here are the rules. Have fun!

Rules of *The Dot Game*

Game Board

- The game is played on a rectangular grid of dots. Consider the horizontal or vertical distance between dots to be one unit in length.

Object of the Game

- To create squares with sides one unit long on the game board by drawing line segments to connect the dots.

Playing the Game

- The game is designed for two players (pair up with a partner in your class).
- Choose a player to make the first move.
- The first player will connect two dots with a line segment that is horizontal or vertical. The line segment must be only one unit long.
- The second player will connect two dots with another line segment that is horizontal or vertical. Again, the segment must be only one unit long.
- Players take turns drawing one-unit line segments.
- If a player completes a square, the player places a mark (an initial, for example) in the square and continues their turn by making another line segment. A player's turn continues until a line segment is made that does not complete a square.
- Play continues until all dots are connected by line segments and the game board is filled with squares belonging to either player.

Winning the Game

- The player who creates the greatest number of squares during the game is the winner.

Play the game two times with your partner, keeping track of the number of squares each person claims. Use the game boards provided. Good luck!

Game Board 1

Game Board 2

The Dot Game

Part I

1. Who won each of the two games?

2. In each game, how many squares did the winner mark?

Game 1	Game 2

3. In each game, how many squares did the loser mark?

Game 1	Game 2

4. What is the combined number of squares for both players in each game?

Game 1	Game 2

5. How many small squares make up the large square on a game board?

6. What is the area of a small square?

7. What is the area of the large square?

8. Draw the largest shape made of adjacent squares you marked.

9. What is the area of the shape above? How did you determine the area of the shape?

10. Rewrite the part of the directions labeled "Winning the Game" using the concept of area.

The Dot Game

Part II *The Dot Game II*

11. Look at Game Board 1 from the previous games and identify the largest shape made with your initialed (or marked) adjacent squares. Draw the outline of the shape on the game board below. Do not draw any interior segments.

12. How many one-unit line segments are there around the outside of the figure that you drew above?

13. Below, write and compare your answer for Question 12 to your partner's answer. The player with the largest number just won *The Dot Game II*!

The rules for playing *The Dot Game II* are identical to those for the original *Dot Game*, except the winner is determined differently. Instead of the winner having the greatest number of squares, the winner in this game has the longest distance around a shape formed by adjacent squares claimed by one player.

Play the game twice with your partner. Remember, the winner has the longest distance around their largest figure made of adjacent squares.

14. What geometric concept does this game address?

The Dot Game

15. How did you determine the **perimeter** of your figure? Explain below.

16. Is it possible for a player to win the original *Dot Game* and lose at *The Dot Game II*? Explain below, using examples and diagrams.

The Dot Game

Part III

17. Betty and Andy played *The Dot Game* on the 4 × 5 grid shown below. Each segment drawn is 1 cm in length and each square has an area of 1 cm². Betty (B) claims she won, while Andy (A) claims he won. How can both be correct? Explain your decision.

A	A	A	A	A
B	B	B	B	A
B	B	B	B	A
B	B	B	B	A

18. Betty won the original *Dot Game*.

   a. Describe the figure formed by Betty's squares.

   b. How many squares did Betty mark?

   c. Describe the reason Betty won, based on the definition of winning in Question 10.

   d. Recall that the dots are 1 cm apart. Describe the area of one of the squares Betty marked.

   e. What is the area of the region marked by Betty? Use units in your answer.

19. Andy won *The Dot Game II*.

   a. Describe the figure formed by Andy's squares.

   b. How many squares did Andy mark?

   c. Describe the reason Andy won, based on the definition of winning for *The Dot Game II*.

   d. Recall that the dots are 1 cm apart. Describe how you found the perimeter of Andy's figure. Include units of measure in your answer.

20. Can you use the same units to describe the reasons that both Betty and Andy won their games? Explain below.

Your teacher will give you some squares with which to build additional rectangles.

21. Make a figure that has the same area as Betty's figure, but with a different perimeter. Use the square tiles to form your figure and draw a diagram below to explain.

22. Make a rectangle that is formed by 16 squares.

    a. What is the perimeter of the rectangle? What is the area? Include units in your answer, and draw a diagram below of your rectangle.

    b. Can you make a different rectangle with the same area and a different perimeter? If so, draw a diagram and explain below.

    c. Can you make a different rectangle with the same perimeter as the rectangle in Part (a) but with a different area? If so, draw a diagram and explain below.

23. What patterns have you noticed about the area of a rectangle? List them below.

24. Write a rule, in words, to determine the area of a rectangle.

25. If a rectangle has length l, width w, and area A, write an equation that relates all three variables.

26. Write a rule, in words, to determine the perimeter of a rectangle.

27. If a rectangle has length l, width w, and perimeter P, write an equation that relates all three variables.

The Dot Game

Title of Model Instructional Unit: The Dot Game

Embedded Assessment Question # _____ Page # _____

How could you improve your response to this question?

What part of this Model Instructional Unit is an example of your best work? Explain why you feel this is your best work.

What mathematical skills, strategies, or knowledge that you had prior to starting this Model Instructional Unit helped you to complete this activity?

What new mathematical skills, strategies, or knowledge did you obtain while completing this Model Instructional Unit?

Middle School Mathematics I

Play Area

Contents

Play Area

Part I

1. Pictured below is an aerial view of a playground. Decide what type of playground equipment each figure below represents. Write your decision next to the label.

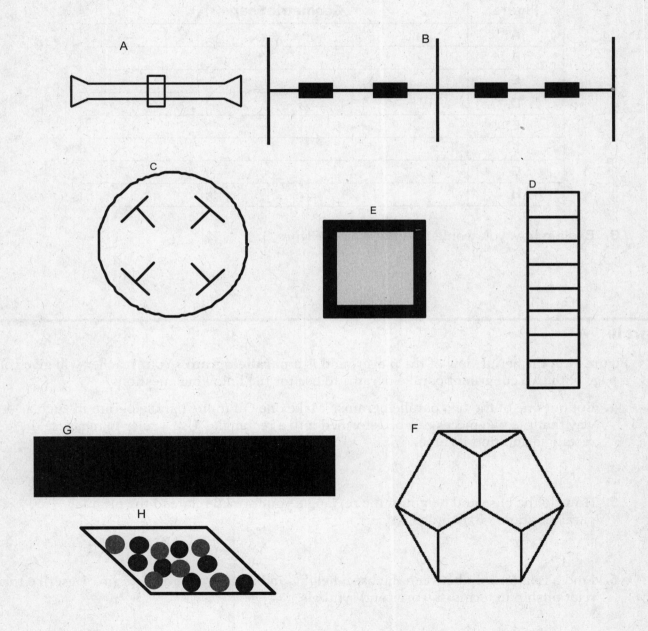

Play Area

STUDENT ACTIVITY (continued)

When designing the layout of a playground, you must know how much area is taken up by each piece of playground equipment. The shapes of the playground equipment are combinations of circles and **polygons** such as rectangles, triangles, parallelograms, and trapezoids.

2. Identify all the geometric shapes you see in the aerial view of the playground equipment. Fill in the table below.

Figure	Geometric Shape(s)
A	
B	
C	
D	
E	
F	
G	
H	

3. Explain how you would find the area of Figure G.

Part II

Figure H in the aerial view of the playground is a **parallelogram**. Your teacher will give you a page with two congruent parallelograms to use for the following questions.

4. Cut out one of the two parallelograms. Make one cut in the parallelogram in such a way that the two pieces can be reformed into a rectangle. Use a ruler to measure the rectangle and find its area.

5. How do the base and height of the rectangle you formed relate to the original parallelogram? Explain below.

6. Find a relationship between the base, height, and area of a parallelogram. Describe that relationship in terms of words and symbols.

SpringBoard™ Mathematics with Meaning
©2005 College Entrance Examination Board

Middle School Mathematics I • Play Area
Student Version 2.0

208

Play Area

Part III

In the playground diagram on the first page of this Unit, Figure F is a hexagon and is made up of **triangles** and **pentagons**. First investigate how to find the area of a triangle.

7. Your teacher will give you a sheet showing two congruent triangles.

- Cut out one of the two triangles.

- Label one of its sides b.

- Draw the segment that represents the height of the triangle to side b and label the segment h.

- Cut out the second triangle.

- Place the two triangles together to form a parallelogram whose base is the side you labeled b.

8. How does the area of each triangle compare to the area of the parallelogram you formed in Question 4? Explain below.

9. Using words or symbols, describe a method for finding the area of a triangle.

Part IV

Recall that the end of Figure A looks like the figure below. This figure is called a **trapezoid**.

10. Your teacher will give you a sheet showing two congruent trapezoids.

- Cut out the two congruent trapezoids.

- The parallel sides of a trapezoid are called the **bases**. Label the bases of each as b and B. Put labels on the inside of the figure. (See figure below.)

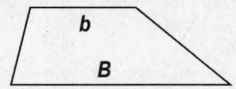

- Draw in the height of the trapezoid and label it h.

- Flip one trapezoid so that the short base of one lines up with the long base of the other.

- Place them together to form a parallelogram.

11. What is the height of the new parallelogram? How does it compare to the height of the original trapezoid?

12. What is the base of the new parallelogram? How does it compare to the base of the trapezoid?

13. What is the area of the new parallelogram?

14. What is the area of one of the trapezoids used to form the new parallelogram?

STUDENT ACTIVITY (continued)

Part V

15. Using what you have learned about finding the area of rectangles, triangles, parallelograms, and trapezoids, describe a method for finding the area of the pentagon that is part of Figure F in the aerial view of the playground. (See figure below.)

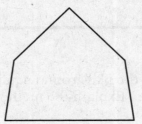

Part VI

Another shape used in the playground diagram on the first page of this Unit can be found in Figure C, a **circle**. Your teacher will give you a circle that has been divided into eight equal parts.

16. Cut the circle into eight congruent pie-shaped pieces. Rearrange the pieces in the pattern started in the diagram below.

17. What shape does the figure you just created resemble?

18. What parts of the circle are approximately the lengths needed to find the area of the figure you named in Question 17?

19. Using words or symbols, describe a method for finding the area of a circle.

Part VII

20. The dimensions of some of the playground equipment are shown in the figures below. Find the area of each figure. Explain the method used for each.

Figure G:

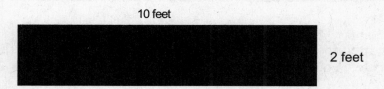

Figure H:

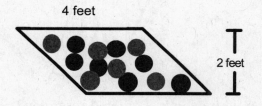

Figure A:

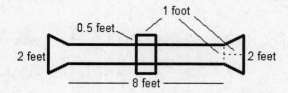

Figure F:

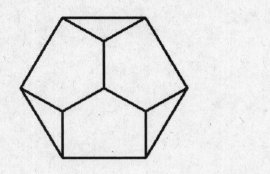

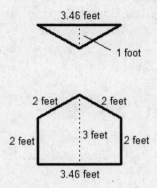

In Figure F, each of the outside segments is 3.46 feet. All of the inside segments are 2 feet. The figure is composed of three triangles and three pentagons. The approximate dimensions of the triangle and the pentagon are shown on the right.

Figure C:

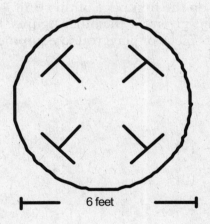

21. Based on the dimensions given for the other figures, make an estimate of the area of Figures D and E. Explain below.

22. Suppose that Figure B on the first page of this Unit is the aerial view of a set of swings. Based on the dimensions given for the other figures, how much playground area is needed to construct this piece of playground equipment? Explain below.

Two Congruent Parallelograms

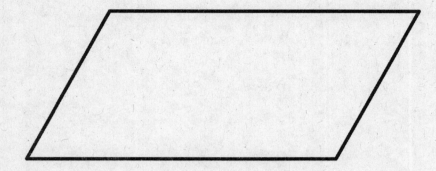

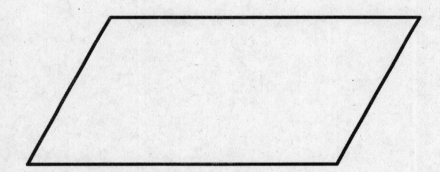

Two Congruent Triangles

Two Congruent Trapezoids

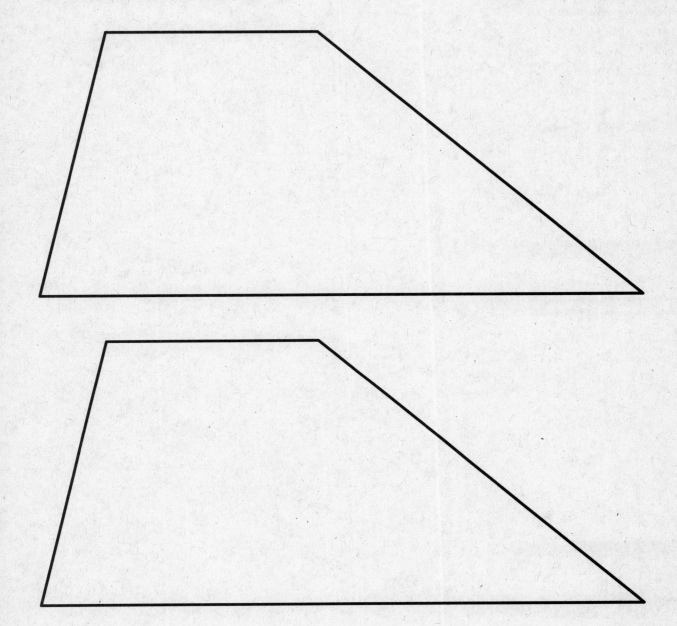

Circle

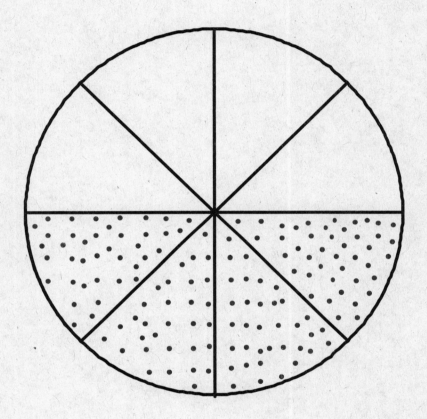

Play Area

Title of Model Instructional Unit: Play Area

Embedded Assessment Question # _____ Page # _____

How could you improve your response to this question?

What part of this Model Instructional Unit is an example of your best work? Explain why you feel this is your best work.

What mathematical skills, strategies, or knowledge that you had prior to starting this Model Instructional Unit helped you to complete this activity?

What new mathematical skills, strategies, or knowledge did you obtain while completing this Model Instructional Unit?

Middle School Mathematics I

Triangle Trivia

Contents

Triangle Trivia

STUDENT ACTIVITY

Ms. Acker asked her students to make up some math games involving facts about triangles. Katie and Allie suggested the following game.

	Triangle Trivia – Perimeter Game
Number of players:	Three to four students
Equipment needed:	Three number cubes and a set of "segment pieces" of the following lengths: 1 inch, 2 inches, 3 inches, 4 inches, 5 inches, and 6 inches.
Directions:	Take turns rolling three number cubes. Using segments from the group's set of the lengths that match the numbers a player rolls, add the perimeter of any triangles that can be formed to that player's score. The first player to reach 50 points wins.

Alex said he did not think that Katie and Allie's game really had anything to do with triangles because all they did was add the three numbers on the cubes and then add that total to their score. Katie and Allie told Alex that there was more to their game than Alex thought.

Triangle Trivia

Part I

1. Play Katie and Allie's game in groups of three or four people to see if what they told Alex is correct. Take turns rolling the three number cubes. Record the results in the table below. Using segment pieces of the lengths that match the numbers you roll on the number cubes, try to form a triangle. If a triangle can be formed, add the perimeter of the triangle to your score. The first player to reach 50 points wins the game.

Player 1:		Player 2:		Player 3:		Player 4:	
Roll of Cubes	Score	Roll of Cubes	Score	Roll of Cubes	Score	Roll of Cubes	Score

2. Is there more to the game than adding the three numbers on the cubes and then adding that total to your score? Explain below.

After playing the game, Alex realized that you cannot always form a triangle from three given lengths. He also found that he did not actually need to use the segment pieces to tell if a triangle could be formed.

3. Explain how Alex could determine whether a triangle can be formed from three given lengths.

4. Alex's discovery is known as the **Triangle Inequality Property**. Use this property to determine whether a triangle can be formed with the given length sides. Show your work or explain.

    a. $a = 8$
        $b = 6$
        $c = 4$

    b. $a = 3$
        $b = 4$
        $c = 7$

    c. $a = 5$
        $b = 5$
        $c = 5$

    d. $a = 3$
        $b = 3$
        $c = 7$

    e. $a = 7$
        $b = 4$
        $c = 4$

    f. $a = 8$
        $b = 4$
        $c = 5$

    g. $a = 1$
        $b = 2$
        $c = 8$

Triangle Trivia

Alex had an idea that he thought would make Katie and Allie's game more interesting. His idea is described below.

Triangle Trivia – Name My Sides Game

Number of players: Three to four students

Equipment needed: Three number cubes

Directions:
- Take turns rolling three number cubes.

- If you can, form

    a scalene triangle.........................add 5 points

    an isosceles triangle ....add 10 points

    an equilateral triangle.................add 15 points

    no triangle ....add 0 points

- If you are caught making a mistake, deduct 10 points from your last correct score.

- The first player to reach 25 points wins.

Katie said she was not sure if she knew what **scalene**, **isosceles**, and **equilateral** meant. Alex showed her the following examples of each type triangle.

Scalene Triangles	Isosceles Triangles	Equilateral Triangles

5. Based on the examples that Alex showed Katie, write a definition for each type of triangle.

   a. Scalene triangle

   b. Isosceles triangle

   c. Equilateral triangle

6. When playing Alex's *Triangle Trivia – Name My Sides Game*, suppose that your cubes landed on the following numbers. Tell how many points you would add to your score and why.

   a. 1, 6, 4

   b. 3, 2, 4

   c. 1, 4, 1

   d. 6, 6, 4

   e. 5, 5, 5

7. Play the *Triangle Trivia – Name My Sides Game*.

Player 1:		Player 2:		Player 3:		Player 4:	
Roll of Cubes	Score	Roll of Cubes	Score	Roll of Cubes	Score	Roll of Cubes	Score

Part II

Besides naming or classifying triangles by their sides, you could also classify them by their angles as shown in the examples below.

Acute Triangles	Obtuse Triangles	Right Triangles

8. Write a definition for each type of triangle.

   a. Acute triangle

   b. Obtuse triangle

   c. Right triangle

9. Label each triangle in the table above Question 8 as scalene, isosceles, or equilateral.

Triangle Trivia

10. Draw a triangle described by each pair of words below or state that it is not possible. If it is not possible, explain why not.

scalene, right	isosceles, right	equilateral, right
scalene, acute	isosceles, acute	equilateral, acute
scalene, obtuse	isosceles, obtuse	equilateral, obtuse

Below you will find a description of one more game created by Ms. Acker's class. Try playing this game in groups of three or four.

Triangle Trivia – Triangle Trio Game

Number of players: Three to four students

Equipment needed: One set of *Triangle Trio* cards. (All sides of equal length and all right angles are marked on the cards.)

Goal: To be the first player to make two sets of three like triangles. The like triangles can be alike when classified by either sides or angles; for example, three acute triangles in one set and three equilateral triangles in a second set.

Directions:
- Deal all the cards face down to the players so that each has an equal number.

- Players pick up their cards. If any player can make two like sets of three cards that player wins the round.

- If not, each player chooses one of their cards to pass to the player on their left. The players again try to make two like sets of three cards to win the round.

- Play continues in this manner until someone wins the round.

- Use the answer sheet to verify that the winner was correct.

Triangle Trivia

STUDENT ACTIVITY (continued)

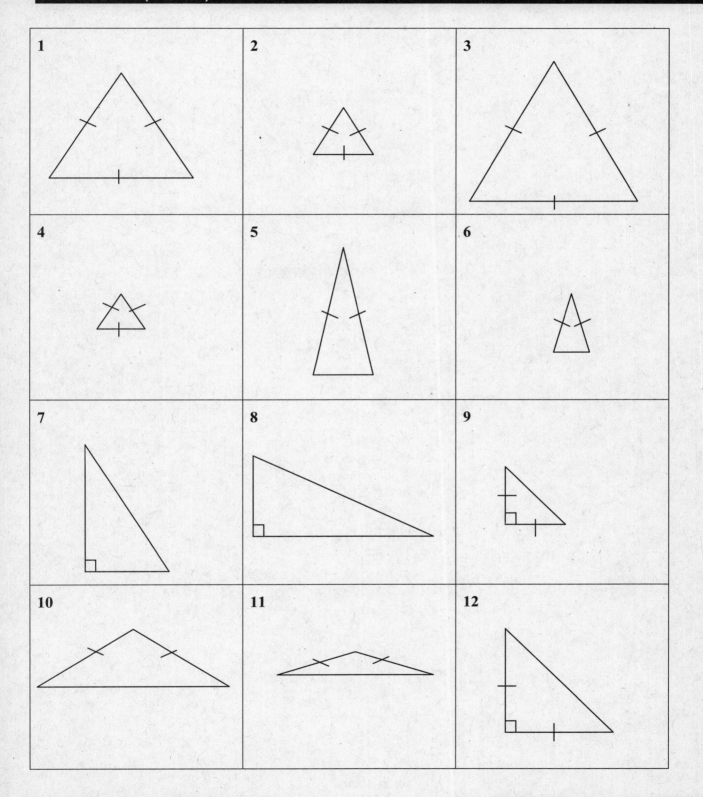

13	**14**	**15**
16	**17**	**18**
19	**20**	**21**
22	**23**	**24**

Triangle Trio Game – Answer Sheet

1	2	3
equilateral acute	equilateral acute	equilateral acute

4	5	6
equilateral acute	isosceles acute	isosceles acute

7	8	9
scalene right	scalene right	isosceles right

10	11	12
isosceles obtuse	isosceles obtuse	isosceles right

13	14	15
scalene obtuse	scalene acute	scalene acute

16	17	18
scalene obtuse	scalene acute	scalene obtuse

19	20	21
scalene obtuse	isosceles acute	scalene obtuse

22	23	24
isosceles obtuse	scalene right	scalene obtuse

Triangle Trivia

Title of Model Instructional Unit: Triangle Trivia

Embedded Assessment Question # _____ Page # _____

How could you improve your response to this question?

What part of this Model Instructional Unit is an example of your best work? Explain why you feel this is your best work.

What mathematical skills, strategies, or knowledge that you had prior to starting this Model Instructional Unit helped you to complete this activity?

What new mathematical skills, strategies, or knowledge did you obtain while completing this Model Instructional Unit?

Middle School Mathematics I

Nutrition Fun

Contents

Nutrition Fun

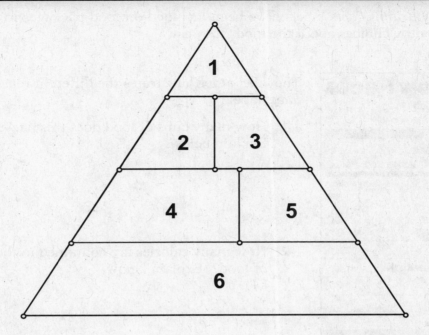

The United States government is interested in helping its citizens eat a healthly diet. Based on research, the Food Guide Pyramid was used by the U.S. Department of Agriculture (USDA) from 1992–2005 to help people visualize the guidelines for healthy eating. Do you know what constitutes healthy eating according to the USDA and the Department of Health and Human Services?

Make a conjecture about which food groups belong to which labeled area of the triangle, then match the number of servings that should go with each labeled area of the triangle.

Food Groups	Area of Pyramid
Bread, cereal, pasta	
Fats, oils, sweets	
Fruit	
Meat, beans, nuts	
Milk, yogurt, cheese	
Vegetables	

Number of Servings	Area of Pyramid
6–11 servings	
2–3 servings	
Use sparingly	
2–3 servings	
3–5 servings	
2–4 Servings	

Nutrition Fun

Since 1994, *Nutrition Facts* labels have been included on food packages to assist consumers in making healthy choices about the foods they eat.

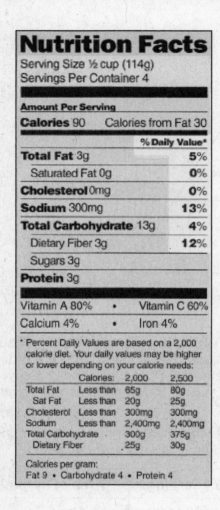

The label at left illustrates the different regions of a *Nutrition Facts* label.

1. How many cups of food does this package contain? Explain below.

2. How many calories are contained in the entire package of food? Explain below.

3. How does the number of calories from fat in a single serving compare with the total number of calories from fat in the entire package? Explain below.

4. The recommended daily amount of dietary fiber is 25g (25 grams). Verify that the amount of dietary fiber in one serving is 12% of the recommended daily amount.

5. A gram of carbohydrates contains four calories. How many calories from carbohydrates are in a single serving? How many calories from carbohydrates are in the total package?

6. What percent of the recommended 2000 calories per day do the carbohydrates in a single serving of this food represent? Explain below.

7. According to the lower portion of the *Nutrition Facts* label, healthy individuals should consume less than 65g of total fat per day. If an individual consumes the maximum of 65g of fat per day, what percent of the recommended total of 2000 calories is from fat?

8. According to this package label, one serving will provide 13% of the daily value of sodium. Sodium, fat, and cholesterol are food components that people attempt to minimize in their diets to maintain good health. Based on this information, how many grams of sodium constitute the maximum amount recommended for a person to consume in one day? Explain below.

Below is a partial *Nutrition Facts* label on a snack food package for a single serving. (A 2000-calorie-per-day recommended diet is assumed.)

	% Daily Value
Total Fat 6g	10
Saturated Fat 1.5g	7
Cholesterol < .005g	1
Sodium 0.21g	9
Total Carbohydrates 9g	3
Dietary Fiber 1g	4

9. Determine the total number of grams recommended for each category below.

Category	Total Number of Grams
Total Fat	
Saturated Fat	
Cholesterol	
Sodium	
Total Carbohydrates	
Dietary Fiber	

10. How did you calculate your answers in Question 9?

Nutrition Fun

11. The *Nutrition Facts* label on a peanut butter jar gives the information below for a single serving. One serving is considered to be 2 tablespoons or 32g. Calculate the number of grams that constitute 100% of the Daily Value for each category. (A 2000-calorie-per-day recommended diet is assumed.)

Category	Grams in a Single Serving	% Daily Value	Total Number of Grams
Total Fat	16	25	
Saturated Fat	3	15	
Cholesterol	0	0	
Sodium	.15	6	
Total Carbohydrates	7	2	
Dietary Fiber	2	8	

12. The FDA recommends no more than 65g of total fat daily.

   a. What percent of the 65g does the 6g of total fat from the label in Question 9 represent?

   b. What percent of the 65g does the 16g of total fat from the label in Question 11 represent?

13. The information above Question 9 shows that 6g of total fat represents 10% of the Daily Value. The information above Question 12 shows that 16g of total fat represents 25% of the Daily Value. Did your answers to Questions 12(a) and (b) agree with those values? Explain below.

14. The peanut butter jar label indicates that a single serving contains a total of 190 calories, with 130 calories from fat. It also indicates that there are 16g of fat in a single serving. For this serving, calculate the number of calories per gram of fat.

Nutrition Fun

Andy is watching her fat intake and decides to compare the total fat in some of her favorite sandwiches to the number of calories from fat. She assembles the data below.

Sandwich	Total Fat (in grams)	Calories from Fat
Hamburger	10	92
Cheeseburger	14	127
Fat Chuck Burger	19	169
Fat Chuck Cheeseburger	31	280
Flaky Fish Supreme	25	228
BBQ Chicken Deluxe	22	195

15. Plot the data from the table above as a scatter plot on the grid below. Label your axes using calories from fat for the vertical axis and total fat grams as the horizontal axis.

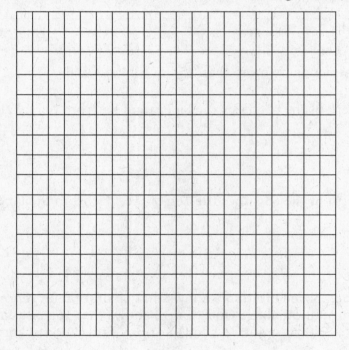

16. Use the data in the table to calculate the average number of calories per gram of fat in the sandwiches that Andy likes to eat.

17. Andy's friend likes to eat a half-pound mega-cheeseburger that has 43g of fat. Predict the number of calories from fat from the half-pound mega-cheeseburger. Explain below.

18. FDA labels indicate there are nine calories for each gram of fat. Does your scatter plot in Question 15 support this fact? Explain below.

Tim refers to the FDA *Nutrition Facts* label below to make healthy choices about the food he eats.

Nutrition Facts		
Serving Size ½ cup (114g)		
Servings Per Container 4		
Amount Per Serving		
Calories 90	Calories from Fat 30	
		% Daily Value*
Total Fat 3g		**5%**
Saturated Fat 0g		**0%**
Cholesterol 0mg		**0%**
Sodium 300mg		**13%**
Total Carbohydrate 13g		**4%**
Dietary Fiber 3g		**12%**
Sugars 3g		
Protein 3g		
Vitamin A 80% • Vitamin C 60%		
Calcium 4% • Iron 4%		

* Percent Daily Values are based on a 2,000 calorie diet. Your daily values may be higher or lower depending on your calorie needs:

	Calories:	2,000	2,500
Total Fat	Less than	65g	80g
Sat Fat	Less than	20g	25g
Cholesterol	Less than	300mg	300mg
Sodium	Less than	2,400mg	2,400mg
Total Carbohydrate		300g	375g
Dietary Fiber		25g	30g

Calories per gram:
Fat 9 • Carbohydrate 4 • Protein 4

Nutrition Fun

STUDENT ACTIVITY (continued)

19. Below is the comparison data Tim has gathered on two snack foods he is considering eating. Make your calculations based on a 2500 calorie diet for Tim.

Tasty Chocolate Bar	% Daily Value	Healthy Granola Bar	% Daily Value
245 total calories	%	180 total calories	%
105 calories from fat	%	50 calories from fat	%
12g of fat	%	6g of fat	%
9g of saturated fat	%	1g of saturated fat	%

Determine the % Daily Value for each of the entries above where the % symbol appears.

20. Tim weighs 160 pounds and decides that he can eat either snack as long as he exercises enough to burn the calories. If he walks uphill at a speed of 3.5 mph, he can burn 7.1 calories per minute. How long will he have to walk uphill to burn the total calories in the Healthy Granola Bar?

21. When Tim plays ice hockey, he burns 9.4 calories per minute. How many minutes would he have to play to burn the calories in the Tasty Chocolate Bar?

Nutrition Fun

Title of Model Instructional Unit: Nutrition Fun

Embedded Assessment Question # _____ Page # _____

How could you improve your response to this question?

What part of this Model Instructional Unit is an example of your best work? Explain why you feel this is your best work.

What mathematical skills, strategies, or knowledge that you had prior to starting this Model Instructional Unit helped you to complete this activity?

What new mathematical skills, strategies, or knowledge did you obtain while completing this Model Instructional Unit?

Middle School Mathematics I

Batter Up! First Inning

Contents

Batter Up! First Inning

Cards for U, a new baseball card company, has hired you to compile statistics for its line of baseball cards. You decide to look at the statistics of some major league players to help prepare for your assignment.

Data tables for three prominent Major League Baseball players follow.

Sammy Sosa

Year	AB	H	2B	3B	HR	BB	TB	BA	SLG
1989	183	47	8	0	4	11			
1990	532	124	26	10	15	33	215	.233	.404
1991	316	64	10	1	10	14	106	.203	.335
1992	262	68	7	2	8	19			
1993	598	156	25	5	33	38	290	.261	.485
1994	426	128	17	6	25	25	232	.300	.545
1995	564	151	17	3	36	58	282	.268	.500
1996	498	136	21	2	40	34			
1997	642	161	31	4	36	45	308	.251	.480
1998	643	198	20	0	66	73	416	.308	.647
1999	625	180	24	2	63	78	397	.288	.635
2000	604	193	38	1	50	91			
2001	577	189	34	5	64	116			

Batter Up! First Inning

Mark McGwire

Year	AB	H	2B	3B	HR	BB	TB	BA	SLG
1986	53	10	1	0	3	4			
1987	557	161	28	4	49	71	344	.289	.618
1988	550	143	22	1	32	76	263	.260	.478
1989	490	113	17	0	33	83	229	.231	.467
1990	523	123	16	0	39	110			
1991	483	97	22	0	22	93	185	.201	.383
1992	467	125	22	0	42	90	273	.268	.585
1993	84	28	6	0	9	21			
1994	135	34	3	0	9	37	64	.252	.474
1995	317	87	13	0	39	88	217	.274	.685
1996	423	132	21	0	52	116	309	.312	.730
1997	540	148	27	0	58	101	349	.274	.646
1998	509	152	21	0	70	162	383	.299	.752
1999	521	145	21	1	65	133	363	.278	.697
2000	236	72	8	0	32	76			
2001	299	56	4	0	29	56			

Barry Bonds

Year	AB	H	2B	3B	HR	BB	TB	BA	SLG
1986	413	92	26	3	16	65	172	.223	.416
1987	551	144	34	9	25	54	271	.261	.492
1988	538	152	30	5	24	72			
1989	580	144	34	6	19	93	247	.248	.426
1990	519	156	32	3	33	93	293	.301	.565
1991	510	149	28	5	25	107			
1992	473	147	36	5	34	127	295	.311	.624
1993	539	181	38	4	46	126	365	.336	.677
1994	391	122	18	1	37	74	253	.312	.647
1995	506	149	30	7	33	120			
1996	517	159	27	3	42	151	318	.308	.615
1997	532	155	26	5	40	145	311	.291	.585
1998	552	167	44	7	37	130			
1999	355	93	20	2	34	73	219	.262	.617
2000	480	147	28	4	49	117			
2001	476	156	32	2	73	177	411	.328	.863

Batter Up! First Inning

Part I

1. What is the meaning of the heading of each of the columns? Place a check next to each heading for which you think you can write a definition and then write that definition.   Next, ask the other students in your group which headings they know and write any definitions you did not already have. With your group, make a table listing the meanings of each heading.

    AB

    H

    2B

    3B

    HR

    BB

    TB

    BA

    SLG

2. Why is it important to know what each column means?

Use the data from the tables to answer the following questions.

Batting average is the decimal number rounded to three decimal places that represents the ratio below.

$$BA = \frac{\text{number of hits}}{\text{number of at bats}}$$

3. a. Write the ratio that represents the batting average for each of the three players in 1997.

   b. Explain the meaning of each ratio in Part (a).

4. a. Convert each of these ratios to a decimal number. Explain your method completely.

   b. Explain any advantages of expressing the ratios in decimal form.

5. Confirm that the batting average for each of the players in 1997 is correct. Did your decimal numbers differ from those in the tables? If so, explain how.

6. Have each person in your group choose three or four years and find the batting averages for those years for each player. Then complete the batting average column for all three players using your group's answers.

7. In which year did each player have his highest batting average?

8. Who had the highest batting average in any one year?

9. Who has the highest career batting average? Clearly explain how you determined your answer.

10. If a player has h hits and b at bats, write an **expression** for the batting average of the player. Explain, in words, the meaning of the expression.

Part II

If a player has five singles, then the player has five **total bases**. If a player has five doubles, then the player has 10 total bases. If a player has five triples, then the player has 15 total bases. If a player has five home runs, then the player has 20 total bases.

11. Given this information, explain how to determine the total bases for a player who has seven singles, four doubles, two triples, and three home runs.

12. Write a mathematical expression that can be used to find the total bases for the player in the previous question.

13. Notice that there is no column for singles (one-base hits). How can you use the information provided in the tables to determine the number of singles? Find more than one method and explain.

14. Write a mathematical expression for the total bases for a player who has s singles, d doubles, t triples, and h home runs. Explain below.

15. Using the information above, confirm that the total bases for each of the three players in 1997 is correct. Show all work.

16. Have each person in your group choose three or four years and find the total bases for those years for each player. Then complete the total bases column for all three players using your group's answers.

Part III

Slugging percentage is defined as the decimal number that is equal to the ratio below.

$$SLG = \frac{\text{total bases}}{\text{at bats}}$$

Note that the Slugging Percentage is NOT a percentage, but instead is a decimal.

17. Write the ratio that represents the slugging percentage for each of the three players in 1997.

18. Convert each of these ratios to a decimal number. Explain below.

19. Confirm that the slugging percentage for each of the players in 1997 is correct. Did your decimal numbers differ from those in the tables? If so, explain how.

20. If slugging percentage were defined as a percent, what would be the slugging percent for each of the three players? Explain how you would convert each number into a percent.

21. Have each person in your group choose three or four years and find the slugging percentage for those years for each player. Then complete the slugging percentage column in the tables for all three players using your group's answers.

22. In which year did each player have the highest slugging percentage?

23. Who had the highest slugging percentage for one season?

24. Who has the highest career slugging percentage? Clearly explain how you determined your answer.

25. Use your variable expression from Question 14 to write another expression for the slugging percentage of a player who has b at bats. Explain below.

26. Ted Williams was a famous baseball player who played from 1939 to 1960. In 1941, he had a remarkable season. Complete the table below for Ted Williams.

Year	AB	H	2B	3B	HR	BB	TB	BA	SLG
1941	456	185	33	3	37	147			

27. Why do you think Ted Williams' season is widely considered to be one of the best ever by a baseball player?

Batter Up! First Inning

Title of Model Instructional Unit: Batter Up! First Inning

Embedded Assessment Question # _____ Page # _____

How could you improve your response to this question?

What part of this Model Instructional Unit is an example of your best work? Explain why you feel this is your best work.

What mathematical skills, strategies, or knowledge that you had prior to starting this Model Instructional Unit helped you to complete this activity?

What new mathematical skills, strategies, or knowledge did you obtain while completing this Model Instructional Unit?

Middle School Mathematics I

Batter Up! Second Inning

Contents

Batter Up! Second Inning

The local newspaper noticed your good work while you were employed by *Cards for U*. The newspaper hired you to make the baseball statistics in the newspaper more understandable to the average reader. You are now looking for ways to represent the statistics of some major league players.

The table below contains home run data for three prominent Major League Baseball players for the period from 1986 to 2001.

Year	Home Run Totals for Sammy Sosa	Home Run Totals for Barry Bonds	Home Run Totals for Mark McGwire
1986	–	16	3
1987	–	25	49
1988	–	24	32
1989	4	19	33
1990	15	33	39
1991	10	25	22
1992	8	34	42
1993	33	46	9
1994	25	37	9
1995	36	33	39
1996	40	42	52
1997	36	40	58
1998	66	37	70
1999	63	34	65
2000	50	49	32
2001	64	73	29

Part I

Batting average is the average number of hits for each at bat. We can also find averages for other data given.

1. The **mean** (also known as the **average** or **arithmetic mean**) for each player's home run production can be determined. Find the mean number of home runs per year for each of the players. Clearly explain your method for finding these averages.

2. Who averaged the most home runs per year? How many did he average?

The **median** is another measure used to compare information about the home run production of each player.

3. What is the median of the home run data for Sammy Sosa? Explain how you determined the median.

4. What is the median of the home run data for Barry Bonds and Mark McGwire? Explain how you determined each median.

5. What differences in the table of data affected the way you found the median for these players? Explain below.

Part II

You are asked by the newspaper to create a visual display of data for the three players to be used to compare their respective home run production. We will investigate different types of data graphs to be used to compare the home run data.

6. In the space below, create a **bar graph** to show the average number of home runs per year by player for the years shown in the table.

7. What conclusions can a reader of the newspaper make based upon the appearance of your graph? Explain below.

8. Create three bar graphs, one for each player's yearly home run totals for the years 1997–2001.

9. What conclusions can you make based on these bar graphs? Explain below.

10. Is there a way you can combine the three bar graphs into one graph? If so, create that graph and explain.

11. What conclusions can you make based on this graph?

Part III

In Questions 3 and 4, you were asked to determine the median of each of the players' home run totals. A **box-and-whisker plot** is a graph that uses the median and other measures to illustrate data.

The following problem gives instructions for making a box-and-whisker plot. First read the directions. Are there any directions that are unclear to you? If so, then ask your group members or your teacher for clarification. Next, follow the directions and complete Question 12 by yourself. Then pair up with another person and compare your resulting box-and-whisker plots.

12. Make a box-and-whisker plot for Sammy Sosa's home run data using the instructions below.

- First, determine the median of the home run data. Write the median in the space below.

- Next, write all the data less than the median. Find the median of this part of the data. This is called the **first quartile**.

- Now write all the data that is greater than the median. Find the median of this part of the data. This is called the **third quartile**.

- Now draw a horizontal number line with an appropriate scale that extends beyond the minimum and maximum of the data. On top of the number line, draw a rectangle whose left side is at the first quartile and whose right side is at the third quartile. Then draw a vertical line in your rectangle that is at the median. This is the **box** part of the box-and-whisker plot.

- Next, draw a dot to the left of the box that corresponds to the **minimum** of the data. Connect that dot to the rectangle with a horizontal line. Now draw a dot to the right of the box that corresponds to the **maximum** of your data. Connect this dot to the rectangle with a horizontal line. These are the **whiskers** of your box-and-whisker plot.

13. What conclusions can you make based on the box-and-whisker plot for Sammy Sosa? Explain below.

14. Create box-and-whisker plots for the yearly home run data for Barry Bonds and for Mark McGwire.

15. Compare the box-and-whisker plots for each of the three players. What conclusions can be made about the home run production of the players? Explain below.

Batter Up! Second Inning

Part IV

The newspaper is writing an article about Henry Aaron, a baseball player who has 755 home runs and holds the record for the most home runs in a career.

16. Complete the following table for the total number of home runs hit by each player during the years 1986 to 2001. (For example, if a player hit 10 home runs one year, seven home runs the next year, and three home runs the next year, he would have a total of 20 home runs.) The totals for the first four years are entered for you.

Year	Total Number of Home Runs for Sammy Sosa	Total Number of Home Runs for Barry Bonds	Total Number of Home Runs for Mark McGwire
1986	–	16	3
1987	–	41	52
1988	–	65	84
1989	4	84	117
1990			
1991			
1992			
1993			
1994			
1995			
1996			
1997			
1998			
1999			
2000			
2001			

17. In the space below, create a **multiple line graph** to show the total number of home runs by player for the years shown in the table.

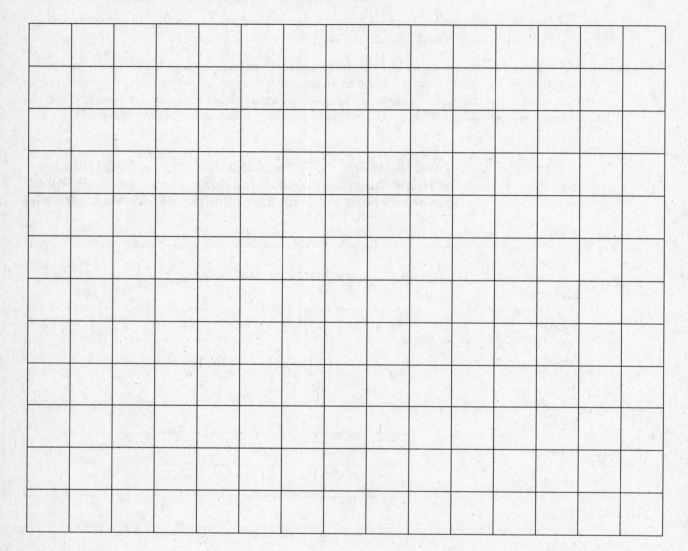

18. If each of the players continued to play past 2001, which one would you predict to first break Henry Aaron's record of 755 home runs? Explain below.

Batter Up! Second Inning

Title of Model Instructional Unit: Batter Up! Second Inning

Embedded Assessment Question # _____ Page # _____

How could you improve your response to this question?

What part of this Model Instructional Unit is an example of your best work? Explain why you feel this is your best work.

What mathematical skills, strategies, or knowledge that you had prior to starting this Model Instructional Unit helped you to complete this activity?

What new mathematical skills, strategies, or knowledge did you obtain while completing this Model Instructional Unit?

Middle School Mathematics I

Appendices

Appendix I

Strategies: Definitions, Purposes, and Icons

Mathematics with Meaning – Middle School Mathematics I

The lists that follow are separated into *Reading*, *Writing*, *Problem Solving*, and *Collaborative* strategies and include a definition for each strategy, a purpose for using the particular approach, and an icon that will be used to identify that particular strategy throughout the teacher materials. These lists appear in the student materials so that you can begin thinking about your own learning styles and identify what helps improve your abilities.

When effective strategies are combined with engaging and challenging material, students will be able to reach the highest levels of success.

STRATEGY	DEFINITION	PURPOSE
❶ Chunking the Text	Grouping a set of questions together for specific purpose(s).	Provides opportunity to establish prerequisite knowledge, assess student understanding, maintain student focus, and establish content connections.
❷ Graphic Organizer	Assisting in visualization of information through maps or frames.	Encourages comprehension and discussion by asking students to transform information from one form to another.
❸ KWL Chart (Know, Want, Learn Chart)	Allowing learners to activate prior knowledge by asking learners to identify what they **k**now, set a purpose by asking what they **w**ant to know, and reflect on new knowledge by asking what they **l**earned.	Helps learner to organize, access, and reflect on learning, which increases comprehension and engagement.
❹ Marking the Text	Selectively highlighting, underlining, and/or annotating text for specific purposes.	Helps learner identify and organize important information.
❺ PACA (Predicting and Confirming Activity)	Making guesses and thinking ahead about what information will be presented in the text. Predictions may be based on visual clues, such as illustrations and headings. Learners will confirm or modify their predictions.	Works best when a reader has some prior knowledge of the topic. Keeps learner actively involved by making, checking, and correcting predictions based on evidence in the material.

STRATEGY	DEFINITION	PURPOSE
❻ Questioning the Text	Developing questions about the text as it is being read.	Creates focused readers who form their own questions, seek out answers, and lead their own discussions.
❼ Read and Think Aloud	Reading the material aloud and describing the thinking process used to make sense of the text.	Assists the oral learner in visualizing and understanding the problem.
❽ Role Play	Assuming the role of a character in the material.	Assists learners in interpreting significant, often implied information, in a problem.
❾ Summarizing/ Paraphrasing/ Retelling	Requiring learners to restate, in their own words, essential information expressed in text.	Assists learner in comprehension, recall of text, and problem solving.
❿ Visualization	Asking students to picture (mentally and/or literally) what they read as they encounter text.	Increases reading comprehension and promotes active engagement with text.

STRATEGY	DEFINITION	PURPOSE
1 Graphic Organizer	Organizing thoughts and ideas in the form of flow charts and webs.	Gives learners an alternate system for beginning the writing process.
2 Journal	Collecting examples of written student responses, reactions, and interpretations.	Assists in formative assessment and provides opportunities to reflect on learning.
3 Quickwrite	Creating quick, informal responses to an oral prompt with time constraints.	Generates multiple ideas in a quick fashion, taps prior knowledge, assesses prior learning, or develops into a longer piece of writing at a later time.
4 RAFT (Role of Writer, Audience, Format, and Topic)	Writing formally with clearly identified **r**ole of writer, **a**udience, **f**ormat, and **t**opic.	Provides focus for formal writing component.
5 Self-Editing/Peer Editing	Improving an initial draft of an explanation, alone, or as part of a group.	Allows learner to examine work carefully, noting the clarity, organization, completeness, and mathematical efficiency of response.

Mathematics with Meaning – Middle School Mathematics I

STRATEGY	DEFINITION	PURPOSE
1 Act Out the Problem	Using objects or students to examine relationships between, and among, the information given.	Keeps the learner actively involved, and encourages visualization of information and relationships.
2 Draw a Sketch	Creating a sketch or diagram to represent data.	Clarifies the information or data given in a problem, and allows the learner to manipulate the data.
3 Guess and Check	Guessing the solution to a problem, checking for accuracy, and using the information obtained to make a more reasonable guess.	Provides a way for the learner to enter a problem; provides a single solution, or pathway, for a more formal solution.
4 Identify a Subtask	Breaking the problem into smaller pieces, each of which needs a solution.	Groups the data given into more manageable pieces.
5 Look for a Pattern	Organizing data in a problem, then observing and extending the data by observing a pattern.	Often used in conjunction with a table or organized list, provides a solution to some problems; permits a generalization for most problems.
6 Make a Table or Organized List	Using a graphic organizer to keep track of the data in a problem.	Organizes information and/or computations systematically; usually used with other strategies to provide solutions.
7 Simplify the Problem	Using "friendlier" numbers to solve a problem, or reducing the number of items in a problem.	Provides insight into the problem and clarifies the operation or strategy needed to solve the actual problem.
8 Work Backward	Tracking a piece of data in the final answer back through the solution process to the starting point.	Provides a way for the learner to enter a problem; provides a single solution, or pathway, for a more formal solution.
9 Write a Number Sentence	Representing the data in a problem with an equation.	Often used in conjunction with other strategies, permits an efficient solution to a problem.

STRATEGY	DEFINITION	PURPOSE
❶ Debriefing	Eliciting student responses in a whole class discussion.	Analyzes and deepens student understanding of content and process chunks.
❷ Group Presentation	Working collaboratively, students present information in a variety of formats.	Provides opportunities for learners to present collaborative solutions to problems and to share responsibility for delivering information to an audience.
❸ Jigsaw	Grouping individuals into teams; team delegates are assigned to expert panels to study material or to perform a task. Upon returning to the team, delegates share their expert knowledge.	Requires students to depend on, and learn from one another, to facilitate understanding of a large body of material by breaking it into smaller, more manageable tasks.
❹ Think-Pair-Share	Thinking a problem through alone, pairing with a partner to share ideas, and concluding by sharing with the class.	Enables learners to construct their own responses to a problem, test and revise their ideas, and consider and interpret the ideas of others.

Appendix II

Student Portfolio and Student Reflection Sheet

Mathematics with Meaning – Middle School Mathematics I

The Student Portfolio is an important tool that is used to organize your work in this course. The portfolio will provide direction as you **revisit** your work and **reflect** upon what you have learned throughout the year. The teacher will guide you to include items in the portfolio that illustrate a wide range of work. You will be given the opportunity to reflect on what you have learned and to summarize important mathematical content and strategies.

Purpose

- To give students a specific place to feature their work and a means to share it with others

- To provide evidence of students' mathematical growth over the course of the year

- To allow students to review the mathematical content and processes they experience in a Model Instructional Unit and to reflect on the new concepts learned

Selection and Organization of Portfolio Entries

The Student Portfolio may be maintained in a two pocket folder, file folder, or three-ring binder and may contain:

- An initial Student Reflection Sheet or student autobiography with goals for the year

- A cover sheet for each Model Instructional Unit that includes general student reflections and identifies Embedded Assessment Questions in the Unit

- Completed Model Instructional Units, arranged in the order that the Units were completed

- Assessment Questions embedded within Model Instructional Units, scored by the teacher using a rubric to indicate growth

- Reflections on each Model Instructional Unit regarding the students' experience with specific mathematical content or processes

- Periodic diagnostic assessments from the College Board

- A year-end reflection on the students' mathematical growth during the course, both in mathematical content and processes

- Projects and assessments made by the teacher

The teacher may modify elements of the portfolio requirements.

Each Model Instructional Unit includes a sheet like the one illustrated on the following page. After completing the activities and assessments in a Unit, you will fill in the answers to the reflective questions. This will assist the teacher and you to better understand how you are progressing through the course in regard to your understanding of the mathematics, the problem solving strategies, and the quality of your work.

STUDENT REFLECTION SHEET

Title of Model Instructional Unit:

Embedded Assessment Question # _____ Page # _____

How could you improve your response to this question?

What part of this Model Instructional Unit is an example of your best work? Explain why you feel this is your best work.

What mathematical skills, strategies, or knowledge that you had prior to starting this Model Instructional Unit helped you to complete this activity?

What new mathematical skills, strategies, or knowledge did you obtain while completing this Model Instructional Unit?

Name: _____ Date: _____ Class: _____

Centimeter Grid Paper